MANUAL

OF

BLACKSMITHING

BY

JOHN R. SMITH

EXPERT BLACKSMITH AND HORSESHOER

CHICAGO

M. A. DONOHUE & COMPANY

Manual of Blacksmithing

by John R. Smith

Originally published by
M. A. Donohue & Company
Chicago

Original copyright 1902

Reprinted by
Lindsay Publications Inc
Bradley IL 60915

ISBN 1-55918-128-1

1994

4   5   6   7   8   9   0

MANUAL OF BLACKSMITHING

CHAPTER I.

FORGES AND APPLIANCES.

It is but fitting that the first chapter of a hand-book on the art of the blacksmith should contain descriptions of the various appliances necessary to the performance of the work. The principal of these are noticed in this chapter, descriptions of the hand tools being given in the next chapter; descriptions of those appliances that require to be specially made for individual jobs are included in the explanations of the processes further on. Brief notices of some of the principal forges will be useful as a guide to the choice of one. Portable bellows forges, both rectangular and circular, are made in a great many sizes. One with a hearth measuring about 25 in. by 18 in. is sufficiently large for a single-handed worker, and in it bar iron up to 1 in. or 1¼ in. square may be heated. For heavier work, requiring the aid of a hammer-man, the hearth may measure 33 in. by 26 in., and range thence up to 39 in. by 30 in. for the largest work. The common forge built of bricks or stone is suitable for average and occasional heavy work.

Fig. 1 illustrates a medium size forge with half hood; it is adapted for machinists, plumbers, miners, marble workers, millers, repair shops, farmers and locksmiths.

Fig. 2 illustrates the noted Standard Lever Black-

smith Forge. The lever motion used on this forge
has been in use for fifteen years, and is now on over
225,000 forges and blowers throughout the world.

Fig. 1.—Illustrates a Medium-Size Forge.

The Joint Brass Oscillating Journal Bearings which
is a feature of this forge prevent all twisting and
binding of the bearings. The oil chambers, when
filled, hold oil for lubricating the bearings automat-

Fig. 2.—Illustrates Standard Lever Blacksmith Forge.

ically six months, or 153 working days, without
further attention. The brass bearings are adjustable over the entire length of the bearings, with

hardened steel lock nut end-screws, for takin up all wear on the fan. Another special feature is the slope bottom coal box, which is beneath the level of the bottom, thus being entirely out of the way. Wet or damp coal is often very necessary when heavy work is being done, and no forge is complete without a sloped coal box.

A lever blacksmith blower is illustrated by Fig. 3. In this forge the lever motion is perfect in its construction, and cannot get out of order; it is light

Fig. 3.—A Lever Blacksmith Blower.

running, with a continuation of momentum between strokes, keeping the blast regular and powerful. It has a 16-in. fan and 25-in. fly-wheel, with a capacity of a 50-in. bellows.

Fig. 4 illustrates a horseshoer's forge. This has been designed and substantially constructed for horseshoers, blacksmith's fires. It is easy running and noiseless, and, when thoroughly known, will be appreciated by every blacksmith who makes a specialty of shoeing horses. The blast is powerful enough for all kinds of light and heavy blacksmith's work, including the heaviest railroad work.

A smith's bellows is illustrated by Fig. 5, and this can be obtained in sizes varying from 24 in. to 40 in. long.

A fan blower is especially adapted for blowing

Fig. 4.—Illustrates a Horseshoer's Forge.

forge fires, boiler fires, steam boiler furnaces, puddling and heating furnaces, dry rooms, refrigerators, or for ventilation, and is illustrated by Fig. 6.

Fig. 5.—Illustrates a Smith's Bellows.

A blower is undoubtedly the best; its equal and continuous blast is superior to the spasmodic, variable, and intermittent current from bellows. There are several kinds of blowers used in portable forges, but there is not very much to choose between them. In workshops a row of forges will be supplied with blast from a single fan or blower, each forge being furnished with a throttle valve in its tuyere pipe.

Fig. 6.—Illustrates a Fan Blower.

The old-fashioned bellows are still found in country shops; but in the modern establishments a fan blast or a blower is used, either being superior in all respects to the bellows.

In small forges, the tuyere is a simple tube. The thickening-up of the nozzle serves to preserve it from destruction for a very long period, and the casting, when burnt away, is replaced. But in all large forges operated by powerful blast, the tuyere

Fig. 7.—The American Wrought Anvil.

is surrounded with water, which protects the nose from the destructive heat of the fire.

The American wrought anvil (Fig. 7) ranges in weight from about sixty pounds up, and is made of steel-faced wrought iron. A double-piked anvil is shown by Fig. 8 and a farrier's anvil by Fig. 9. The conical end (A) or "beak" is used for turning bars upon, and the hole (B) is for the reception of the anvil chisel, and various bottom tools. Care should

Fig. 8.—Double Piked Anvil.

be taken that the edges of the anvil are not bruised.

The anvil is supported so that its face is about 22 in. high from the ground by a stand which is often a block of wood. The anvil is prevented from slipping sideways by spikes driven into the wood close alongside the anvil-feet. An iron stand (Fig. 10) is much firmer than one of wood, though its first cost is greater.

Fig. 9.—Farrier's Anvil.

The anvil wears hollow on the surface in the course of time, and its edges become rounded; the less this occurs the better, as an anvil needs to be true when flatting over large surfaces and square corners. Occasionally, but very seldom, the beak is broken off, either as the result of faulty construction or very rough usage.

The ordinary tail or standing vice is, on the whole, as good as any. Vices with parallel jaws and instantaneous grip arrangements used by fitters are scarcely suitable for the smithy, where the work is mostly of a rough character. The tail-vice may be attached to a regular bench put up in the smithy, or a small bench only two or three feet in length may be attached to the wall near the forge, and the vice fastened to that; or it may be self-contained, standing on a tripod framework of wrought iron, and so be movable about the shop.

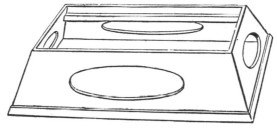

Fig. 10.—Anvil Stand.

In a shop not provided with steam power, the Oliver hammer is a useful tool, and may easily and cheaply be rigged up by smith and carpenter; though not so rapid in its action as a steam-hammer, it is the best substitute for one. If power is available, the drop-hammer is an improvement on the Oliver, and is employed in many large firms. The steam-hammer is, however, the most efficient, but it consumes a large quantity of steam, requires the attendance of a man to operate the valves, is costly, and therefore only suitable to large shops.

Figs. 11 and 12 show a front and a side view of an Oliver hammer, as often fitted up in country shops, where the appliance is often entirely home-

made. A, A, are stout wooden posts driven deeply
into the ground, between them being pivoted on
dead centers a piece of wood, B, of either round or
square section.   Iron centers are driven into the
end of B, and these are pivoted upon studbolts, C, C.
The pivots and the countersunk holes should be
case-hardened, and iron bands, D, D, should be shrunk
on to prevent the wood, B, being split out at the
ends. The hammer-shaft, E, is mortised into B, over

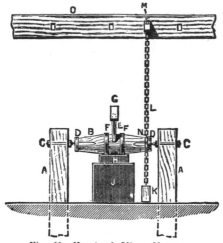

Fig. 11.—Front of Oliver Hammer.

which, on each side of the hammer-shaft, bands, F, F,
are shrunk, to prevent the concussion of the hammer blows splitting the wood.   The hammer-head,
G, is recessed as shown, to receive top swages, and
corresponding bottom swages are let into the anvil,
H, which, in turn, rests upon a massive anvil-block, J.

The Oliver hammer is worked by the smith with
his foot upon the treadle-board, K, to which one end
of a chain, L, is attached, the other end being fast-

ened to a flexible wooden pole, M. A short lever, N, is fastened to the chain between K and M, and this lever being driven into B, of which it forms a part, moves B on its pivots and causes E and G to descend with the treadle, K. On the release of the foot, G is pulled up by the spring bar, M, which is tenoned into a stout beam, O, which is fastened to the wall. There are several forms of drop hammers, a com-

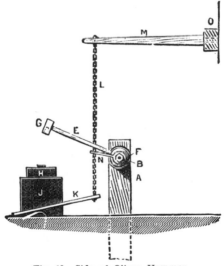

Fig. 12.—Side of Oliver Hammer.

mon arrangement being to attach the hammer to the lower end of a belt which is fastened to a pulley, the latter being revolved as required by friction cones, operated with a disengaging clutch. When the latter is released the hammer falls; on again throwing it into gear, the hammer is lifted. The clutch is controlled by means of a lever handle, within easy reach of the attendant.

A monkey or swinging pendulum hammer is illustrated by Fig. 13. It is made of cast iron, and is balanced carefully on its center of gravity by the correct setting in position of the eye, B, which is cast into the bar. The battering end is preserved from fracture, and from too rapid wear, by means of the wrought-iron band, c, which fits around, and is shrunk into a shouldered recess of dovetailed section. The handle, or porter, D, is of wrought iron cast into the monkey. It is provided with an eye, through which a small chain or rope, E, is passed; by means of this the monkey is pulled backwards after every blow. The monkey is suspended by a chain, A, from any convenient beam overhead. It is

Fig. 13.—Swinging Monkey.

drawn back several feet from the perpendicular, and then let go; being heavy, it strikes the iron with great force.

The smith's mandrel, Fig. 14, a conical hollow casting, is employed chiefly in making rings, as will be explained, and should be kept in three or four sizes.

An appliance employed for rounding off the heads of bolts is shown in plan and elevation by Figs. 15 and 16. A is a bracket-like casting, bolted firmly to a heavy cast-iron base let into the ground. Through an overhanging boss at the top of A slides the shank of the rounding tool, B. This is plumb over a bolster, C, on the base. The bolt is dropped into the bolster, C, and the tool, B, struck upon it with a sledge hammer. The support, D, is merely for the purpose of support-ing the rounding tool while the bolt is being slipped

Fig. 14.—Sugar-loaf Casting.

into the bolster. It is pivoted to a strap fastened to the side of A, and is turned to one side when the tool is being struck with the hammer.

A bolt-forging machine is power-driven, and by its means bolts and their heads are formed between dies having a rapid vertical movement imparted from a long cam shaft. Where bolts are made in even moderate quantities, the bolt-machine soon pays for itself. An almost necessary adjunct to this machine is the power-driven hot and cold iron saws. The first is a comparatively thin saw, run dry at a high rate of speed, that cuts roughly through red-hot

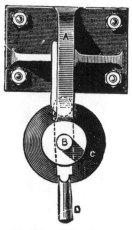

Fig. 15.—Plan of Appliance for
Rounding Bolt Heads.

rods and bars almost instantly. The second is a thicker saw, that cuts slowly, but smoothly and cleanly, running in water the while.

Two forms of carriers are commonly employed to move and carry about bars which are too long to be manipulated by the tongs. One (Fig. 17) is used underhand, being carried vertically with the hook lowermost, and the work, or one end of it, slung in the hook. The other (Fig. 18) is used for heavy forgings, being carried by two men. When one end of the work is carried thus, the other may be

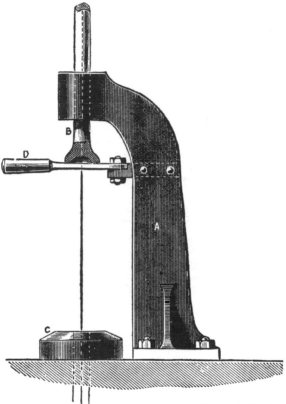

Fig. 16.—Elevation of Appliance for Rounding Bolt Heads.

slung in the crane, or be merely supported with the tongs, or balanced by other means.

Long rods and bars, when being cut off or

welded, require some support at the end farthest
away from the smith. Support is also wanted when
two rods are being welded by a single-handed
worker; one rod is held by the smith, but the other
has to be supported by some mechanical contrivance.
which should be provided with some means of adjusting the height, to suit differences in the bulk
or thickness of the work. Contrivances of this kind

Fig. 17.—Carrier for Bars.

are shown in Figs. 19 and 20, and both, of course, are
portable. In the one shown by Fig. 19, two cheeks, A,
of wrought iron, cut to the outline shown in the end
view, and maintained at a definite distance apart
with the stay bolts, B, B, are pierced with numerous
holes, C, at different heights. Into any of these
holes the bolt, D, can be inserted, carrying the loose
roller, E, that supports the work.

In the second contrivance (Fig. 20), two uprights.
A, are tenoned into a foot, B. Between the uprights

Fig. 18.—Carrier for Bars.

'the forked piece, C, slides, and by the insertion of
pins, D, D, in any pair of the series of holes in the
uprights the height of the fork, and consequently of
the work, is regulated.

Sometimes the support consists simply of a
forked end screwed into a socket, and turned up or
down with the hand; the adjustment of this appliance is more exact than in the others.

Another method of supporting heavy work is by
means of an endless sling chain dependent from a

loose pulley, slung from a light jib overhead. This contrivance is often used simply for lifting work of considerable bulk from the fire to the anvil and back again. For heavier work a pair of pulley blocks are often slung from a jib, and then there is mechan-

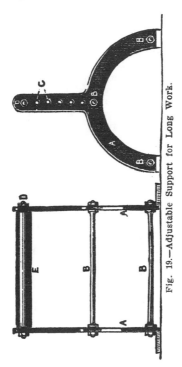

Fig. 19.—Adjustable Support for Long Work.

ical gain, and facility for raising and lowering the work as well.

Fig. 21 shows a simple and effective rig-up for manipulating heavy work. Use is made of the movable jib, which is an accessory to most forges. It is pivoted against the wall, and upon its cheeks, A, A, runs the jenny, B, consisting of four wheels and carriage, with a depending hook, C, to which is attached a lever having a long arm, D, and a short arm, E. At the end of the short arm is a square nut, F, threaded to take a coarse, square-threaded screw, G, which passes up clear by the side of the crane. At the lower end of this screw is a swivel, H, through

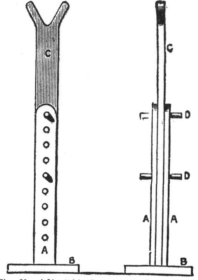

Fig. 20.—Adjustable Support for Long Work.

which the screw works, being turned by a lever passing through the hole in the boss at the lower end of the screw, G. From the lower end of the swivel depends the chain and clip in which the work is suspended. Adjustment of the height of the work can be made by turning the screw, G, the range of height being equal to the length of the screw, and by pulling at the chain, J, at the long end of the lever. This latter, being rapid and immediate in action, is used during the manipulation of the work. The exercise of very little force, such as a man can

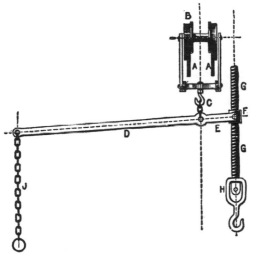

Fig. 21.—Apparatus for Lifting Heavy Forgings.

apply with one hand, is sufficient to raise and lower the work upon the anvil or the bending block, and to move it to any position required.

CHAPTER II.

HAND TOOLS.

The smith's miscellaneous small hand tools, though numerous, consist mostly of appliances for molding or shaping metal into diverse forms. Like the tools used in some other trades, many are made as occasion requires, and accumulate quickly.

The smith's hammers, other than power-driven, are of two kinds—the hand hammer and the sledge. The first-named weighs from ½ lb. to 1 lb., and generally is of the form shown in Fig. 22, with the ball

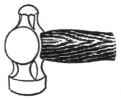

Fig. 22.—Ball Peen Hammer.

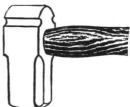

Fig. 23—Sledge Hammer.

peen. The cross peen hand hammer is used for fullering and drawing down. The flat face is used for striking heavy blows and for finishing surfaces. The sledges are of one of the two forms shown in Figs. 23 and 24, and weigh from 4 to 14 lbs., one of from 6 to 8 lbs. weight being about the average. Fig. 25 shows the method of wedging on the head to prevent it from flying off. Hammer handles should be kept in a dry place for several weeks previous to use; if they are not well seasoned, they shrink with the heat, and are apt to work loose on their heads.

The necessary firing tools are the poker, Fig. 26,

the slice, Fig. 27, and the rake, Fig. 28. Their uses are obvious.

Before any forging can be done, tongs are necessary. There are often a dozen tongs to a moderately well appointed forge, but it is not necessary to get them all at once; a few of the simpler and most necessary tongs will now be described. Each of these tools is made in several sizes to suit the various kinds of work.

Fig. 29 shows the hollow-bit tongs; enclosing and gripping the rod for a length of about 2 in., they take a very firm hold of both rods and bars. When there is a collar or other enlargement at one end of the bar, the pincer tongs, Fig. 30, are

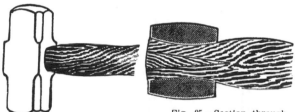

Fig. 24.—Sledge Hammer.

Fig. 25.—Section through Wedged Hammer Head.

sometimes employed to enable a firm grip to be taken; the jaws have V-notches, as shown in the end view. Fig. 31 shows tongs that are more generally useful; the elongation of the V-shaped jaws gives a stronger grip, and the rod or bar is less liable to shift sideways.

When a bar is so long that it cannot be held with these tongs, a crook-bit tongs (Fig. 32) is used; the jaws being turned aside permits the bar to pass alongside the handles on one side of the rivet. The lip serves to retain the bar in place, otherwise it would be apt to slip out sideways. With these four kinds of tongs work can be commenced on round

rods and square bars of iron. For other work there
are other forms. The ring encircling the handles
or reins of the crook-bit tongs is called a coupler,

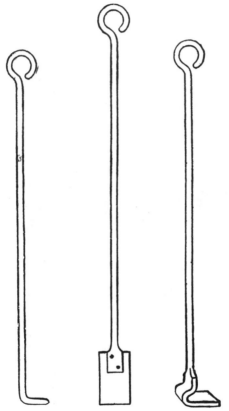

Fig. 26.—Poker.   Fig. 27.—Slice.   Fig. 28.—Rake.

which is slid over the reins, and tightened by a tap
or two with the hammer. The work is thus grasped

without the need of any further effort on the part of the smith.

For holding flat bars, tongs shaped like those

Fig. 29.—Hollow Bit Tongs.

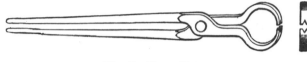

Fig. 30.—Pincer Tongs.

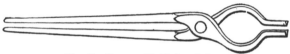

Fig. 31.—Tongs with V-shaped Jaws.

Fig. 32.—Crook Bit Tongs.

Fig. 33.—Tongs for Flat Bars.

Fig. 34.—Tongs for Flat Bars.

shown at Figs. 33 and 34 are employed. In Fig. 33 the jaws are alike, and come into direct opposition. In Fig. 40 a flat jaw falls within the sides of the other. These are made in various widths and proportions, the range of each pair being rather limited. For holding and manipulating rings, hoop tongs (Fig. 35) and pick-up tongs (Fig. 36) are employed.

When work is being reduced to final dimensions, it is necessary to check sizes by tools other than the steel rule. For flat rods the gap gauge is commonly used. It is of the typical form shown in Fig. 37, each gap being of a definite width, and differing from its neighbor by ⅛ in. or 1-16 in. Their depth is unimportant, but bears some proportion to width.

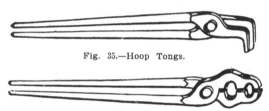

Fig. 35.—Hoop Tongs.

Fig. 36.—Pick-up Tongs.

Fig. 37.—Gap Gauge.

These gaps, which are really fixed calipers, can be used in an instant to embrace and test the dimensions of a red-hot forging.

For circular work, calipers with long shanks are used. Fig. 38 shows a single caliper, whilst Figs. 39 and 40 are two forms of double calipers.

To cut a cold bar, it is nicked round with a cold set (Fig. 41). The bar is laid across the anvil with the chisel-edge upon it, and the chisel, being struck with a hammer, nicks the bar. The bar is rotated slightly and another blow struck, and so on rapidly until there is a sharp indentation all round the bar. Then it is struck sharply across the edge of the anvil and snapped in two at the nicked section.

A hot-set (Fig. 42) is used if a bar is divided while red-hot, and the smith holds it in place while the hammer-man strikes it. The set is driven in

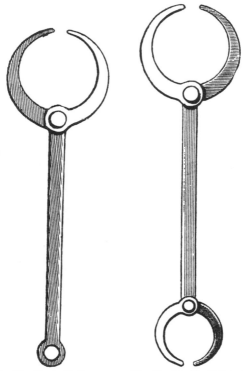

Fig. 38.—Single Caliper.   Fig. 39.—Double Calipers.

deeply, and several blows are given at one spot; and by the time the bar has been turned completely round the set has almost or entirely severed it. In use the set becomes hot, so that it would be liable to lose its temper and become soft; therefore, after every four or five blows on the hot iron, the smith dips it into water to cool it. The hot sets are often provided with handles differing from those of the swages—that is, they are like hammers, but without

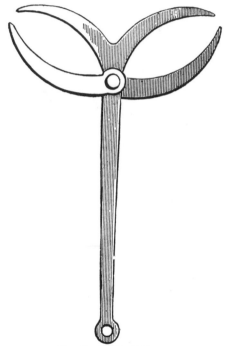

Fig. 40.—Double Calipers.

wedges, which would shrink and become loose, because they are subjected to more heat. When the handle becomes loose, striking its butt end upon the anvil jumps the set down to a firm hold, ready for immediate use. Sometimes they are provided with iron handles, or with withy handles as shown in Fig. 41.

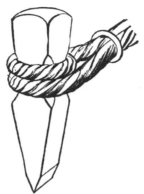

Fig. 41.—Cold Set.

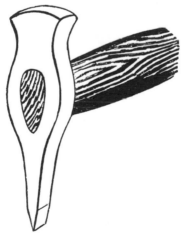

Fig. 42.—Hot Set.

A smith working single-handed when nicking bars uses the anvil cutter (Fig. 43). It is essentially a chisel, having its edge uppermost and a shank fitting into the square hole in the anvil; a bar laid upon it and struck with the hammer is nicked on the under side, and rotating and striking it with the hammer will have the effect of nicking it all round.

The knife tool, Fig. 44, and the curved tool, Fig. 45, are used for cutting lengths off iron bars.

Swages of many shapes are used for a variety of purposes which will be duly explained. Top and

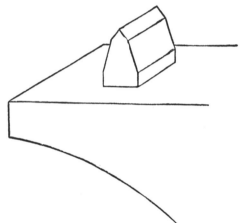

Fig. 43.—Anvil Cutter.

bottom swages are illustrated respectively by Figs. 46 and 47.

A bottom swage like Fig. 48 is very useful, both for bolt making and for general work. Using this, a gradual reduction in diameter can be made without the trouble of changing the separate single bottom swages. A swage for finishing collars is illustrated by Fig. 49.

In the spring swages, Figs. 50, 51 and 52, the top swages guide themselves, and the work can be held in

position and hammered to shape by one operator.
The difference between the three is that, whilst Figs.

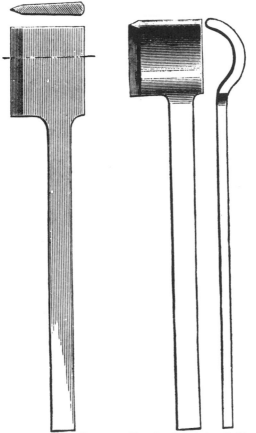

Fig. 44.—Chisel for Cutting   Fig. 45.—Chisel for Cutting
        Iron Bars.   Circular Ends.

50 and 51 each take one diameter of iron, Fig. 52
will take three different sizes. The top and bottom

faces of two, it will be noted, are made flat for use with the hammer, while in Fig. 51 the lower swage has a pin to fit into the anvil, and the upper swage is formed to be struck with the sledge-hammer.

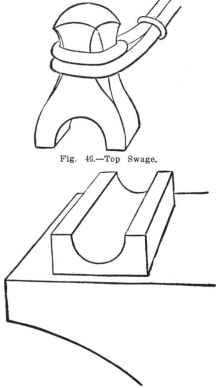

Fig. 46.—Top Swage.

Fig. 47.—Bottom Swage.

The angular swage, Fig. 53, is used in shaping and welding hot metal. The angles support the sides of the metal whilst being hammered, and the work is performed more quickly—an important matter in welding. With this tool, a top swage can be used if desired, or the sledge or steam hammer by itself.

Fig. 48.—Bottom Swage.

Fig. 49.—Swage for Collars.

Fig. 50.

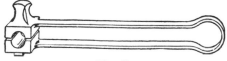

Fig. 51.

In Figs. 54 and 55, similar swages are shown as forming bolt-heads.

The common swage block, Fig. 56, is an appliance

without which no smith's outfit is fairly complete. Its body is pierced with numerous holes—round, square and oblong—and its edges are provided with grooves of various sizes, in circular and V forms. The block is used lying on its side, as a bolster,

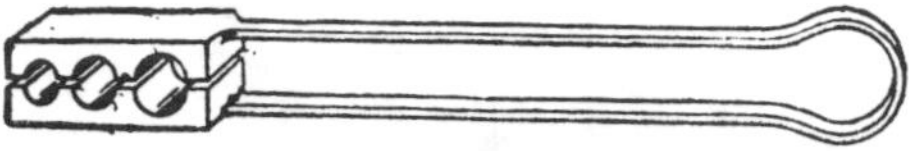

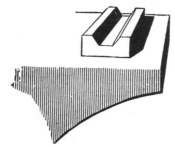

Fig. 52.—Spring Swages.

Fig. 53.—Nut Swage on Anvil.

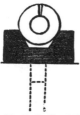

Fig. 54.—Bolt Head Laid in Bottom Tool.

Fig. 55.—Bolt Head Shaped in Bottom Tool.

upon which holes are punched and drifted, and as a heading-tool, upon which shouldered work is finished. When laid upon one of its edges, the grooves serve as bottom swages for circular, hexagonal and rectangular work.

The stand upon which the swage block is mounted may consist of upper and lower cast-iron frames

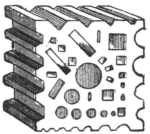

Fig. 56.—Swage Block.

Fig. 57.—Swage Block Stand.

Fig. 58.—Top Fuller.

Fig. 59.—Bottom Fuller.

with the upper one provided with strips, enclosing the block. The two frames are held together by four shouldered wrought-iron pillars, whose pins pass through holes cast in the frames, and are riveted over at top and bottom. Fig. 57 shows a stand.

An essential tool is the fuller, of which four forms are here illustrated; Fig. 58 shows an ordinary top fuller, Fig. 59 the bottom fuller, Fig. 60 the round-faced fuller, and Fig. 61 the hollow fuller. Another form of hollow tool is shown by Fig. 62 as finishing a ring on a V-block. These tools enter into much of the smith's work, as will be made apparent as the subject is pursued.

The flatter, Fig. 63, is held by the smith whilst

Fig. 60.—Round-faced Fuller.

Fig. 61.—Hollow Fullering Tool.

the hammermen strike it with sledges. The cup tool, Fig. 64, is used in the same manner as the flatter.

Punches are circular, square, oval, oblong, and wedge-shaped, and have handles of hazel or iron. A punch, Fig. 65, and a bolster, Figs. 66 and 67, are often used together, the punch, by means of hammer blows, being driven through the red- or white-hot metal placed over the bolster.

Drifts are used to finish holes that have been

punched smaller than the finished dimensions, when
facilities for machining are not available. They are
taper, as in Fig. 68, or parallel tools, having circular,
square, oblong, elliptical, or polygonal cross sections,
corresponding to those of the finished holes. There is
scarcely a limit to the forms in which they may be
made and used. Drifts are smooth, and, being driven

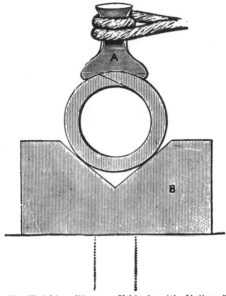

Fig. 62.—Finishing Ring on V-block with Hollow Tool.

through the punched holes, enlarge, shape, and
smooth them while the metal is red-hot. Two drifts
are often employed: one considerably tapering, so as
to enlarge the punched hole; a second, the filler, or
filling-in piece, or mandrel, very slightly tapering,
for imparting the precise finished dimensions.

Smooth drifts are rarely parallel; if they were,

their withdrawal from a hole would be a matter of difficulty; the sides should taper not less than from two to four degrees.

The cutting drift partakes either of the nature of a sharp punch, or of a file. It does not open out

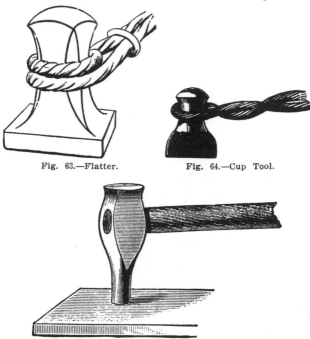

Fig. 63.—Flatter.   Fig. 64.—Cup Tool.

Fig. 65.—Round Punch on Thin Bar.

the hole by pressure, and does not remove a large quantity of material at once; it merely smooths and finishes a hole already nearly to shape and size. Fig. 69 shows a drift for shallow holes, and Fig. 70 for deep ones; they are shaped with files from suitable blanks, and then tempered to a color ranging from brown to purple. Toothed drifts for fine work have the teeth closer together; for coarse, rough work, they are spaced farther apart. They are beveled to allow clearance for the chips, being the equivalent of backing-off in other cutting tools. For hard metal the angle between the cutting edge and

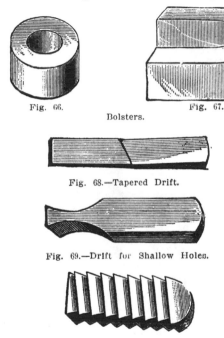

Fig. 66.   Fig. 67.

Bolsters.

Fig. 68.—Tapered Drift.

Fig. 69.—Drift for Shallow Holes.

Fig. 70.—Drift for Deep Holes.

the face is greater than for softer metals, thus following the usual practice in all cutting tools. Oil should be supplied to the edges of the drift, and of the hole when driving it in, and the work should be bedded firmly on a block of metal; and care must be taken that the drift is driven straight. If the hole is deep, the drift must be withdrawn once or twice for clearance of chips. If the hole to be drifted is much smaller than the finished size, it will be necessary to enlarge it by chipping with a chisel.

Drifts with teeth are used for making round holes into square, oval, hexagonal, etc. It is better in these cases to work one-half the hole at a time. Thus, in drifting a round hole into a square one, one-half the round hole would be filled with a half-

Fig. 71.—Drift used in Smoothing Holes.

round plug, and a flat drift used to operate against the other half of the hole, little by little, thin backings being interposed one after the other. When one-half of the square is shaped, it is filled up, and the other half treated similarly. An elliptical hole is shaped in a similar way.

The drift is also serviceable for holes that do not pass quite through the material. As an example, for a rectangular hole to be smoothed in one direction, the drift shown in Fig. 71 could be used. The face, A, would remove a thin shaving. To take a second cut a thin strip of metal would be placed behind the drift; to take a third cut, an additional thin strip; and so on.

For drilling large holes, the ratchet-brace is a good tool. It can be fixed either upon a bench in a permanent position, or where wanted on work in hand. A press-drill thrust down with a lever is also a common appliance in country shops. For a shop where much drilling is done, a double-geared hand or power drill is more efficient.

Dies are used by the smith when the initial cost of making them is likely to be repaid by the increased convenience and time saved. They will be described later.

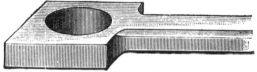

Fig. 72.—Heading Tool.

The heading tool, Fig. 72, is used for finishing the shouldered ends formed on round bars. The hole should be sufficiently large to take the bar whose end it is required to true.

Small tools—as tongs, swages, fullers, flatters, punches, and such like—accumulate in large numbers, and litter the place unless proper methods are employed to keep them in order. Commonly, racks are fixed against the wall by the side of the forge. These are stout iron bars, supported parallel between uprights, at a distance of from 6 in. to 8 in. from the wall; the shanks or handles of the tools are dropped between these bars, their enlarged portions resting upon the top edges. Tool racks are formed against the wall by driving two uprights into the ground at each end, and riveting the horizontal bars of iron to these. The uprights and the bars are of flat iron—say, 2 in. by ½ in.—placed edgewise.

For the lightest tools, handled with withies, or with round rods, it is sufficient to employ as racks short lengths of round rod riveted into flat bars. The flat bars are then secured to vertical uprights driven into the ground and leaning against the wall, and the rods stand out like spike nails. Upon these the light tools are hung by their handles. The flat bars may measure 2 in. by ½ in., and the rods be of ½-in. iron, 5 in. or 6 in. long. These lighter racks should be placed above the racks of parallel bars just previously described.

Another method is to have an oblong open bench or stand of wood rigidly framed together. The top is crossed with bars or rods, leaving open spaces, in which the shanks or handles of the tools drop. Unless there is plenty of floor-room available, this is not so good as the rack, which occupies scarcely any floor-space.

For the heavier appliances used with the steam and other hammers, stands of a different kind are also used. Thus, two cast-iron standards of A form, with three or four pairs of internal brackets, carry between them stout deal planks, which are bolted to the brackets. Upon these deals the heavy spring swages, die-blocks, etc., are laid side by side, the lighter on the top shelves, the heavier beneath, ready to hand.

CHAPTER III.

DRAWING DOWN AND UPSETTING.

Before attempting to execute either of the processes of drawing down and upsetting dealt with in
this chapter, it is necessary that the fire in which
the iron is to be heated be properly made. The
formation of the fire is of far greater importance
than may be supposed.

The "stock" is the term given to the mass of
hard-caked coal on a smith's hearth, within which the
heat is confined; and it also in some degree forms
a reserve of fuel. But its primary purpose is
to prevent radiation of the heat, and to cause its
concentration upon the work in the hearth. If it
were not for the stock, much of the heat would
go up the chimney, and the work also would be
oxidized more rapidly than it is, by reason of its
partial exposure to the air. The size and shape of
the stock evidently depends on those of the work.
The stock consists of two portions—one lying against
the tuyere and hearth-back, the other placed opposite
to the first in the direction of the coal and water
bunks, the work lying midway between the two.
The only portion of the fire that is replenished to
any considerable degree, in the course of a day's
work, is that central portion. The stock, though
highly heated, does not burn away sensibly, because
it is protected from the direct action of the blast,
and the upper portions are kept damp. Yet the
inner faces, being in direct contact with fuel supplied from time to time to the central part of the
fire, are at a glow with heat.

To make a fire, therefore, the stock is first built at the back and front of the hearth, and beaten hard with the slice or with the sledge, the choking of the tuyere hole being prevented by passing an iron rod temporarily into it. The fire is then lit in the central portions with a handful of shavings and a little coal, assisted by a gentle blast.

Forgings of unequal sectional area are formed either by drawing down, upsetting, or welding, or by a combination of the three processes. Generally, the choice between these three methods is not made because one is essentially superior to the other regarded simply as a question of ultimate results, but because under given circumstances it either involves less work or economizes material, or is the only way possible with material that happens to be in stock, or because there are odds and ends that it is desirable to use up; or, lastly, because it is the best method available with the tools and help at the disposal of the smith. The alternative, therefore, is commonly one of expediency.

It is often, however, a question of relative dimensions. If the difference between the enlarged and the reduced part is very great, neither drawing down nor upsetting would be resorted to, unless for some exceptional reason, but welding would be employed. The same holds good in other forging; as, for example, in the case of eyes. An eye having a small hole and much metal around it, as that of the tie-rod of an iron roof truss, would have that end forged solid, and the hole punched through. But an eye having a large hole and relatively little metal around it, and so possessing more the character of a loop, would be bent round and welded. An eye of medium thickness may obviously be made in either fashion.

To draw down a piece or iron, proceed as follows: Suppose the portion marked A. Fig. 73, has to be drawn down from a bar originally of the size of

B. The bar is laid across the edge of the anvil in a slightly inclined direction, and nicked at c, Fig. 74, with a top fuller. If both sides of the bar have to be drawn down, then a bottom fuller would be inserted in the anvil in opposition to the top fuller, and the bar would be nicked as in Fig. 75. Chisels

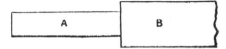

Fig. 73. Square Bar Drawn Down.

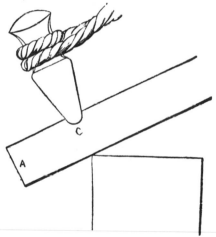

Fig. 74.—Nicking with Top Fuller.

or sets are not used in such nicking, for these would divide the fibers of the metal, while the round-faced fullers simply alter their direction without breaking their continuity.

The preservation of the continuity of the fiber is of primary importance in forged work, so that what may appear to be roundabout methods which give

much extra trouble will often be resorted to in order
to preserve that continuity. Fiber or "grain" should
never be severed. Few of the tools used by the smith
for shaping to outline have absolutely square edges;
they are all more or less rounding. Thus the continuity of the fiber is preserved, however it is bent
and twisted. A bar of iron held in the vice and
bent until it is doubled shows on the outside radius
the torn ends, which look like bundles of vegetable
fiber, and not unlike torn animal muscle. A speci-
men torn asunder in a testing machine has its fibrous
structure still more apparent, though not so clearly
as in the bending process, in which the outer skin
will present a most characteristic striation or shriv-
eling in the longitudinal direction.

Fibrous iron may readily be changed into a weak

Fig. 75.—Bar Nicked with Top and Bottom Fullers.

crystalline material by nicking with a sharp tool,
or by excessive hammering. A bar of iron, nicked
round, and broken off suddenly, shows fractured
surfaces as highly crystalline as those of cast iron.
This clearly proves the necessity of making fullers,
and other shaping or molding tools, with edges
rounding.

When the work has been nicked with the fuller,
the metal along A (Figs. 73 and 75) is drawn down
or thinned by a succession of blows from the hand
hammer or sledge, with or without previous fullering. When fullering tools are used, the top fuller
would be employed singly if only the one face requires reduction, or in pairs, one above the other, if
both faces have to be drawn down. The effect is

that a succession of depressions are formed upon the surface of the spread-out work with ridges between, and these have to be obliterated with the hammer.

Fullering and hammering not only lengthen the bar, but also spread it sideways. If the bar is to be equal-sided, the widening has to be prevented by rapidly hammering the sides alternately with the faces. After every few blows are given on the faces, the smith turns the bar quarter round during the brief interval between a couple of blows, and the iron receives several blows upon the edges as a corrective to those on the faces, and its equal-sidedness is thus preserved during the process of drawing down. By practice, this rapid changing of the faces on the anvil is accomplished without damaging the rectangular form.

In drawing down, whether with fullering tools, or with the hammer alone, as is frequently done where the reduction in area does not amount to much, the process of thinning always commences at the end of the iron farthest from the smith, and proceeds towards himself. One inch and a half or two inches is drawn down at a time, and the work is thus rendered easier than if a larger surface were taken at once.

When the iron is first roughed down, its surface will not be smooth, though a good smith can impart a very fair finish to a flat surface by the hammer alone. The hammers should strike so as to bruise the work as little as possible. There is a knack in using the hammer so that its edges will not mark the work, the blow being given by the central rounding portion of the face only. Striking fair with the middle of the hammer face, each mark serves to partly obliterate others, and leaves a very smooth surface, only slightly wavy. This is all that a smith working single-handed can effect by way of finish. With the assistance of a hammerman the surface can be smoothed more effectually by means of a flatter, which is held with the right hand of the smith, and slid in turn all over the surface of the work while the hammerman strikes it with the sledge. Thus finished, the work is left very smooth.

In drawing down a round bar the process is the same in principle, but slightly different in detail. The rod will be nicked round with a fuller and drawn down under the hammer, beginning as before at the end farthest from the hand. A fullering tool is not used for extending the metal, which is done with the hammer only, and the rod is rotated between each hammer blow. Toward the close of the operation, smoothness is imparted by means of swages, the work lying in a bottom swage of nearly semicircular form, see Fig. 76, which shows an anvil swage fitted into the hole in the anvil, while blows are struck upon the rod's upper surface with a hand hammer, if the smith be single-handed, or, if the smith has a striker, with the sledge upon a top swage the counterpart in form of the bottom. In Fig. 76 A indicates the top and B the bottom swages, with the bar of iron, c, between them; D is the anvil.

By means of suitable spring swages, previously described, a smith, working single-handed, can sometimes make use of the top as well as of the bottom tool.

With a steam hammer this work of drawing down and finishing is very much simplified. It is then not even necessary to use top or bottom fullers, for, having marked the position of the shoulders on the bar, the smith lays the bar on the anvil of the steam hammer, and draws down the work directly between it and the tup or hammer, turning the bar quickly during each period of ascent of the tup. If the bar is of large size and of considerable length, the drawing down will still have to be done in short lengths, two or three inches from the end being drawn down first, and the bar being then thrust farther along, and the succeeding portions drawn down. The bar is always held perfectly flat, and the hammer finishes at once.

For rod work, top and bottom swages of the

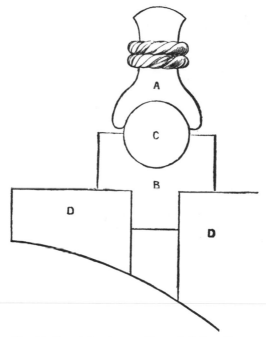

Fig. 76.—Round Bar between Top and Bottom Swages.

spring type are placed under the tup at the finishing stage. The rod is first drawn down roughly between the anvil and the tup, being rotated rapidly between each blow, a rudely circular form being imparted or preserved simultaneously with the process of drawing down. Before the reduction is quite complete, the spring swages are placed on the anvil, held by an attendant, the work inserted between them, and rounded and finished by a few final blows of the tup on the top swage—the work still being revolved during each period of ascent of the tup.

While these processes are being carried out, and with the iron at a red heat, a scale of oxide forms rapidly. The larger the forging, the greater the quantity of the oxide formed. This should be brushed away with a switch of brushwood as fast as it forms, otherwise it will be driven by the hammer blows into the surface of the work, and form a rough scale, which is afterwards both unsightly and a hindrance to easy tooling in the vice or lathe. Where the forgings are large, a man stands by the steam hammer and brushes away the scale after every half-dozen or so blows. At the anvil the striker or the smith knocks the scale off immediately the iron is removed from the fire, and afterwards as often as it may be required.

To judge the length of iron to be allowed for drawing down is not difficult to a practiced smith. Few trouble to calculate in figures the length required. Yet, when working the best and most expensive qualities of iron and steel, it is as well to bear in mind a rule of simple proportion. The original section of a bar bears the same proportion to a given reduced section that the length of the latter bears to that of the former. Thus if a bar originally 3 in. square has to be reduced to an inch square, one inch in length of the 3-in. bar will be taken for reduction to a 3-in. length of one inch square. If the reduced portion is tapered, or of unequal and varying dimensions, then the mean of the various sectional areas must be taken. Additional allowance must be made for ragged and perhaps burnt ends, and a trifle for inaccuracy in cutting off.

The time different smiths will be occupied over a given piece of work differs greatly. A smart smith will always do as much work as possible upon a forging in a single heat. While his iron is in the fire, he will mentally go through the sequence of operations, and see that whatever is required is at hand, and when the iron is on the anvil he will strike quickly while the iron is hot. In some examples to be given, the number of heats in which work ought to be forged will be stated approximately.

Upsetting, or jumping up, is one of the alternatives of drawing down. By this method the metal is knocked or jumped up into a mass larger in area than the bar itself. Upsetting is a slower and more laborious process than drawing down. A smart smith will draw down several inches of bar at one heat; but to upset a very moderate mass of metal will require several heats. Hence it is not possible to treat in this way any very large-shouldered portion; in this case the plan is to weld on a ring or collar, or a solid mass of metal, according to circumstances. Except the iron be cut off sufficiently short to go endwise under the hammer, the use of this tool is not possible in upsetting. However, the monkey, or swinging pendulum hammer, fulfils the purpose of the hand hammer.

The method of upsetting to form a collar, A (Fig. 77), upon the end of a rod whose original section is that of B, and without welding the collar on as a ring, is as follows: The end which is to form A is enclosed in the fire, but no more of that end is heated than the precise amount required to be upset; that portion of the rod which joins it is kept quite cool and black by heaping damp coal around it. The end is then brought nearly or quite to a welding heat, and taken from the fire. Sometimes on removal from the fire, and just before upsetting, the extreme face of the heated end is dipped into the water trough

to chill it, and so the better to prepare it to resist
the blows of the hammer; but this is not always
done.

The actual upsetting is performed in one of sev-

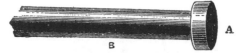

Fig. 77.—Bar with Collar on End.

eral ways. The bar may be held in both hands
(Fig. 78) in a vertical position, and the white-hot
end jumped down repeatedly upon the anvil face, or

Fig. 78.—Jumping
Bar Vertically.

Fig. 79.—Upsetting Bar
Horizontally.

upon the plate of cast iron which is often let into
the ground alongside of the anvil stand for this purpose. Another way is to lay the bar in a horizontal

position upon the anvil face (Fig. 79), holding it in one hand if light, and, with a hand hammer, hammering the end to be upset. Or, if it is heavy, it may be held in both hands, or, perhaps, slung in a chain from the forge crane, and upset with a sledge hammer. When very heavy, it is laid upon the anvil face or upon a leveling block, and the swinging monkey is driven against it.

Three or four heats are often required to jump up a moderate mass of metal. The result is, that fairly exact dimensions are not at once obtainable by this method, as in the case of drawing down. The jumped-up mass of metal, in spite of much care in localizing the heat precisely where it is required, is very unequal, and quite without sharp shoulders. Hence, considerably more metal has to be massed together than is actually required in the completed work, in order to allow of symmetrical finish to size. Upsetting tends to separate the fibers of the metal. It is, therefore, necessary to counteract this by hammering the jumped-up portion at a welding heat. When the metal for the collar is massed in sufficient quantity, it is finished parallel in swages, and the square shoulder finished with a set hammer or flatter, or in swages, and the end with hammer and flatter.

A collar can be also formed upon any portion of a bar situated away from the ends by localizing the heat in the position required, and then jumping up the metal at that particular place, until sufficient mass is obtained for finishing to size and shape. Any other sections can be heated, and the spreading out can be performed by upsetting in one direction more than in others.

CHAPTER IV.

Weldability is one of the most valuable proper ties possessed by wrought iron and mild steel. Welding is often the alternative of drawing down or of upsetting; correct heat and cleanliness are the chief requisites. Welding heat corresponds with that temperature at which the metal is in a state of partial fusion on the surface. At that temperature it is extremely plastic, and a little hammering will cause two surfaces to adhere and possess as much strength as the other parts of the metal. The welding heats for iron and steel differ, and even also the heat for different qualities of iron and different qualities of steel. Any iron will require a much greater heat than steel, and the better the quality of iron, the higher the welding heat that it will stand without becoming burned. At a welding heat iron gives off dazzling sparks; steel shows only an intense yellow, and gives off few sparks. The ascertaining of the correct heat is a matter for experience entirely, and no description or illustration can take the place of practical lessons.

To illustrate the process of welding more clearly, two plain examples, one a collared rod, and the other a plain straight rod, are given.

Taking the shouldered end (Fig. 80), first cut off the rod, A, and then prepare to fit over it the ring, B, for which take a square bar, say ⅛ in. larger than the finished section required, and, with a hot set, cut off one end diagonally or else fuller it down. Then bend the bar roughly into circular form over

the anvil horn (Fig. 81), and cut off to the required
length, with a sloping face to lap upon and match
the first diagonal. The metal must have sufficient lap
to allow for welding, and for dressing off and finish-

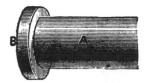

Fig. 80.—Bar with Shouldered End.

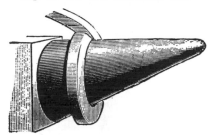

Fig. 81.—Forming Ring on Anvil Beak.

Fig. 82.—Ring slipped over Mandril.

ing. If the ring is fairly true, it will be ready to go
into the fire for welding; but if not, slip it over a
mandrel, Fig. 82, and give the scarfed joint a neat
appearance, either with the hammer alone or with
one of the hollow tools previously described. Then

slip off the ring and flatten the faces (Fig. 83). This is precisely the plan that would be adopted in welding a separate ring.

To weld it to the rod, the ring is slipped over the end of the rod, care being taken to remove any scale adherent to either, and they are then put into the clear fire. Sand may be sprinkled over the work, but with a clear fire it is not necessary, and is frequently not done. When the welding heat is attained, which for wrought iron is of a dazzling whiteness, when the iron seems ready to melt, and particles appear ready to drop off, and a rapid evolution of sparks takes place, the work is removed from the fire, placed on a V-block (B, Fig. 62), and the scarf joint and the ring are hammered all round with a

Fig. 83.—Smoothing Faces of Ring with Flatter.

hand hammer, the rod with its ring being continually turned into fresh positions on the V-block. If a hammerman's services are available, the hollow tool is used, and a few blows upon it consolidate and smooth the surfaces. Then the faces and shoulders are finished by means of a heading tool, having a hole of a size suitable to take the rod, a few blows with hammer and flatter finishing off both the under shouldered face and the upper flat face. Then it may be necessary to work over the circular part again with the hollow tool. This is to finish the surface, for the welding heat is soon past, and if the union of the joint faces is not fully effected in the first few seconds, it will be more or less imperfect.

To weld a rod, a scarfed joint is employed, and plenty of metal is wanted to allow for hammering the joint together and for finishing it afterwards without reducing below correct sizes; therefore, the ends of the bar have not only to be scarfed, but to be slightly upset. The meeting ends, which have been cut off square, are laid horizontally upon the anvil, and are upset or beaten over, while nearly at a welding heat. Then they are laid over the edge of the anvil, and scarfed or beaten down diagonally with a fullering tool, the face of the scarf being made rounding rather than hollow. Both ends having been served precisely alike, they are put back into the fire, and raised to the welding heat. Lift the

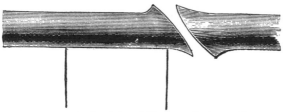

Fig. 84.—Ends Scarfed and Upset ready for Welding.

work vertically out from the fire; do not drag it through the coal. Any particles of dirt that are present will show as dark specks on the white-hot iron, and should be brushed off with a switch of brushwood.

The smith and his helper lay the scarfed ends together, as shown in Fig. 84, and then two or three blows with the hand hammer cause the ends to unite, and the rod can then be rapidly turned about on the anvil while the joint is consolidated all round with hand hammers or sledges. The top and bottom swages can be used for imparting the finish required. It will be apparent that without the first enlargement or upsetting of the rods, the process of welding and swaging would have thinned the rod at the welded section below that of the other portions. How much to upset and how much to scarf are matters for experience.

These notes on welding are somewhat of an elementary character, but further information on the subject will be embodied in the descriptions of working miscellaneous examples.

Punching, drifting, and drilling are the three methods by which the smith commonly makes holes in metal. The first two are performed on red-hot iron and steel; the last, and sometimes the second also, on cold metal. Drifts, and the method of using them, are dealt with in the chapter on hand tools (see pp. 20 to 40), and at present punching alone will be treated upon.

Punches may be used to make a clean, finished hole, to which nothing is done subsequently, and which is quite good enough for its purpose. In other cases, punching, like the coring of castings, takes out the bulk of the metal, leaving a certain small allowance for finishing with drill, reamer or boring tool.

Generally the details of the process of punching are as follows: The iron to be punched, being brought to a suitable heat, full red or white, is laid across the anvil, and the punch is driven by means of blows from a sledge or hand hammer, about halfway through. The punch is then withdrawn, and the iron is turned over and laid upon its opposite face. A dark spot indicates where the chilling effect of the punch has taken place, and enables the smith to set the punch again in position for piercing the metal so that the holes meet. During the formation of the second portion, the work is either laid upon a bolster or over the hole in the anvil, and the punch then passes freely through.

If the hole is deep, the hot iron closes and tightens around the punch, and the latter is therefore withdrawn at every three or four blows. Further, the heat of the iron makes the punch very hot, so that after every three or six blows it is necessary to cool the punch in water.

Methods of producing punched holes vary according to circumstances. If it is desired to preserve the same amount of metal all around, the hole is partly punched and partly drilled or opened out. Obviously, when a hole is punched entirely with a flat-ended tool like Fig. 65, p. 36, the metal removed is equal in area to the area of the point of the punch itself, and the width of the bar is only very slightly perceptibly increased (see Fig. 85).

Fig. 85.—Material removed by
Flat-ended Punch.

Fig. 86.—Commencing Hole
with Hot Set.

Another way of making a hole without weakening the bar to any great extent is by means of a conical punch, which may be inserted, and the hole formed and opened, without the removal of any appreciable quantity of material. Or if a hot set is driven from one side half-way through the bar, and half-way from the other (Fig. 86), a punch or drift can be driven in afterwards, and the slit opened out into circular or oblong form, as may be required.

Long slot-holes are cut in two ways. In one, holes are punched at each end of the intended slot equal to its width, and the metal between is cut out with the hot set, cutting from opposite sides in succession, and meeting in the middle (Fig. 87). In the other, holes are punched at each end, and a chisel cut made centrally from hole to hole, and a drift

inserted and the metal opened out (Figs. 88 and 89).
In this way the flanking metal is thrust out sideways, and the bulk of its section retained. Such a
slot-hole is finished by inserting a drift or mandrel of
the correct section, and hammering the outside edges
of the bar upon it.

When punching holes, it is necessary to take
account of the direction of the fiber. Unless attention is given to this, the iron will become divided
instead of spread out. Punching puts considerable
tension on the fibers around the hole, with reduction
of area, and it is an operation, therefore, that requires to be done with judgment.

Fig. 87.—Slotted Hole; Area Reduced.

Figs. 88 and 89.—Slotted Holes; Area Retained.

To punch slotted cottar ways in which the section of the iron is not enlarged, take a tapered oblong
punch or drift of steel, like that shown at A, Fig. 90,
with rounding ends. Raise the iron to a welding
heat, and properly support it according to its shape,
upon a bolster or a bottom tool, and drive the punch
half-way into it. Turn the iron over, cool the punch
in water, and drive it in exactly opposite to the
first position, until the openings meet at the center
of the bar. The slightly tapered punch makes a
hole doubly tapered, which is also rough. A parallel
drift or filling-piece is then driven into the hole,

which accommodates itself to the form of the filling-piece. The outside of the iron is smoothed and finished, and when the shape is completed the filling-piece is driven out. This method of finishing a job while a central punch, drift, filling-in piece, or mandrel remains in the work, is adopted in many classes of work.

Punching a hole through a stout pin is illustrated

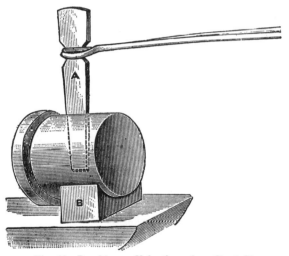

Fig. 90.—Punching a Hole through a Stout Pin.

by Fig. 90, the pin selected being 3¼ in. diameter; the hole measures 1½ in. by ½ in., and is made at one heat. The punch, as shown, has its body below the handle, about 6 in. long, and is tapered. The pin being brought to a white heat, the punch is driven almost through. Then the pin is turned over and the punch driven into the darker spot which has appeared, and the hole is thus completed. During the punching the tool has to be several times cooled in water. At the first stage of making the hole, the pin lies upon an ordinary bottom swage. At the second stage it lies upon a bolster, B, in form like a hollow swage, but pierced with a central hole, through which the drift can find a clear way.

As the hole is thus roughly punched, the metal around it will be partly compressed, partly bulged; very little is actually driven out and removed by the punch. The bulging of the pin is corrected by hammering between top and bottom swages, and then the hole is finished by drifting, all being done during the one heat. During the punching, whenever the punch is withdrawn to be cooled, a little small coal is strewn in the punched hole, to burn up the gas which would otherwise resist the passage of the punch.

CHAPTER V.

The smith works under three conditions, each of which ought to receive separate treatment. These are: first, when he works alone, without the assistance of a striker, or of steam power, or of dies; second, when he has the assistance of a striker or hammerman, but is still without steam power; third, when he has the help of a hammerman, and has also the use of a steam hammer, and dies of various kinds. Amateurs and many country and jobbing smiths come under the first category. Men in small workshops come under the second; whilst the third class embraces the men in large engineering and general iron works.

It is obvious that the particular circumstances under which work has to be performed must often modify the methods adopted. For example, a smith who has the use of a steam hammer will either swage or draw down, when such is practicable, in preference to upsetting and welding. Again, a smith who has command of dies and steam hammer will not spend so much time in finishing and smoothing the surfaces, angles, and corners of his work upon the anvil, because he can put his roughed work between a pair of dies, and finish it with a few blows of the steam hammer. The smith who has no help from a striker will be restricted to the very lightest work. Iron of nearly the finished sizes and sections wanted will have to be used. Extensive drawing down and welding cannot be done; little is possible beyond work that can be done with the

hand hammer. Swages, flatters, fullers, and chisels—
except the anvil cutters—are of scarcely any use
when there is available only one pair of hands for
holding the work and the tools.

The class of work that comes within the range of
the unassisted smith differs from that of the worker
who is favored in the matter of assistance and tools.
But he has still all the wealth of ornamental work,
like that done by mediæval smiths, all tool work—
almost anything, in fact, where the sections of iron
and steel do not exceed, say, 1 in. to 1¼ in. in diameter. Obviously, the choice of forges, tools, as well
as methods of work, will be different under these
several conditions.

In the judicious choice of that which is the best
out of several possible methods, lies much of the
skill of the experienced smith. It by no means follows that a method by which a piece of work can
be forged to shape is necessarily the quickest, cheap-
est, or best; or that which may be the best method
under certain conditions is the best in all or any
circumstances. One often has to adopt a method
which may not be best from another's point of view,
because he either does not possess the iron of proper
sections, or the special tools, or other necessary assistance. This fact is made more forcible when the
numerous sections of iron required by the all-round
smith are considered. Even in large shops, where
steam hammers are available, it is often impossible
to manipulate the heavier sections of iron. These
require very powerful hammers, in order that the
force of their blows shall penetrate to the interior of
the mass. Hence many engineers find it necessary to
order for massive work specially heavy forgings, or
"uses," as they are called at the rolling-mills.

The material of a single-handed smith, and that
of an amateur, is limited to small sections. With a
small forge no great· heat is possible, and a smith

working single-handed cannot manipulate any heavy
sections. Bars of iron are made in lengths of several
feet, and the purchasing of a fair stock of entire
bars of several sizes would prove a heavy expense.
It is best to select a few bars of the most useful
dimensions, according to the class of work which
it is intended chiefly to do, and when any other sections happen to be wanted, to purchase them in
short lengths from a local smith or at an iron store.

The principal shapes of iron used by the smith
are "round," "square," and "flat" bars. These are
made in almost all ordinary dimensions, and in different qualities. The published lists of sections
rolled at some of the best-known iron and steel
works in this country are here made use of.

The bars are rolled in the following Wire Gauge
sizes: 7, 6, 5, 4, 3, 2, 1; and also ranging from 3-16
in. up to 2⅝ in., increasing by sixteenths; from
2⅝ in. to 5 in., increasing by eighths; from 5 in. to
5½ in. by quarters; from 5½ in. to 6 in. by eighths;
and from 6 in. to 6½ in. by quarters; and each of
these can be rolled to "full," and "bare," as well as
to exact sizes. Thus there are obtainable sixty-eight
different diameters of round bar, from 3-16 in. to
6½ in.

The squares increase from 3-16 in. to 1⅝ in. by
sixteenths; from 1⅝ in. to 4 in. by eighths; from
4 in. to 5½ in. by quarters; and from 5½ in. to 6½
in. by half-inches; giving fifty-one sizes in square
sections from 3-16 in. to 6½ in.

The flats range from ⅜ in. to 12 in. wide, in almost all thicknesses from ¼ in. upwards, advancing
by sixteenths and eighths. Flats in sixty-five different widths are obtainable.

This iron is made in four qualities—the "ordinary," or common, "best," "best, best," and "best,
best, best."

Good metal being rather costly, a careful smith

will preserve odds and ends of iron and steel for small work, and for welding to other portions, so saving the cutting off of small pieces from long bars.

It is not economical to buy inferior iron. The quantities used in light work are so small that the saving is scarcely worth taking account of, while inferior iron is a constant source of anxiety to the smith.

The differences in the qualities of iron are broadly these: A good iron is silvery and clean-looking; a bad iron is dull and dirty by comparison. A good iron is free or nearly free from flaws, which in a bad iron always show up when it is brought to a red heat. They are due to the intermixed cinder and scale left by insufficient puddling. The way to get rid of some of these is to subject the iron to a welding heat, and hammer it thoroughly all over to consolidate it in some degree.

Carbon, manganese, phosphorus, and silicon exercise so vital an influence upon the numerous alloys of iron and copper as in many cases to totally and absolutely change its appearance and physical qualities. But in wrought iron, where the foreign ingredients seldom amount to more than 1 per cent, being often only $\frac{1}{2}$ per cent, those very minute admixtures are found to affect the metal to an extent that makes itself very evident at the anvil. The most readily forged, whether hot or cold, is that which is the purest. Iron that will forge well while hot, but not when cold, is said to be "cold short," and this is due to very minute quantities of phosphorus, antimony, and silicon. When iron is apt to develop cracks while being forged hot, it is said to be "hot short," and this may be due to a minute quantity of sulphur, whose amount may not perhaps exceed .03 per cent, or it may be due to antimony. Only delicate chemical analysis could demonstrate the presence of these foreign elements, but the smith sees their results when the iron is under the hammer and punch.

The most striking characteristic of wrought iron that has been rolled is its fibrous condition, and this occurs also, in a lesser degree, in mild steel. This is the quality by which it can be shaped according to the will of the smith. It is a remarkable property of these fibrous materials that the very qualification that is of so much value can be changed or modified in the working. A bar of iron placed across the anvil cutter and nicked around with a chisel, may be broken off short with little effort, and a practiced eye is necessary to detect whether the iron is cast or wrought by the appearance of the fracture, which is wholly crystalline. The same bar bent without nicking, or gradually torn asunder until it breaks, shows the fracture wholly fibrous, the long, string-like fibers becoming drawn out as though the bar had been built up of innumerable fine strings of metal. Again, if a crank-shaft or a lever-arm breaks at a sharp re-entrant angle, the fracture will be crystalline. But if it breaks at an angle whose faces are gradually merged into one another with a curve or hollow, the fracture will be fibrous.

It follows from the fibrous character of wrought iron developed during rolling, that it must be considerably stronger in the direction in which it is rolled (A, A, Fig. 91) than in the transverse direction, B, B. The difference is in about the ratio of 21 to 17—that is, if it would require 21 tons per inch to break the bar through the line B, B, in a direction at right angles with A, A—that is, across the fibers— 17 tons would suffice to break it along A, A—that is, along or with the fibers. This holds good to a very slight extent only in mild steel, where the rolling is only incidental to the shaping. The direction and relative strength of fiber have a most marked influence upon design in wrought iron. It shows why the

direction in which work is subjected to the greater
stress should always coincide with the longitudinal
direction of the fibers; why curved work should not
be cut from the solid, thereby severing the continuity
of the grain, if it is possible to bend it round and so
preserve the fibers continuous.   It shows why in
many cases it is better to split or divide a bar, and
bend or fork it, so preserving continuity of grain,
rather than to slot out or to weld on.   It explains
many practical points in the working of wrought iron
as distinguished from the working of the homogeneous mild steels.   It shows the advantage of keeping

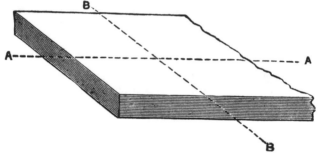

Fig. 91.—Direction of Fibre in Iron Bar.

the edges rounding and not sharp on fullering and
similar tools, by whose use the grain is not violently
severed, but rather bent to shape.

The action of the fuller is typical forging, for it
reduces the surface of the work without leaving
angular marks upon its surface.   It does not cut at
all, but leaves a wavy surface, with fiber perfectly
continuous.   When making a set off in a bar, whether
with the object of reducing its dimensions or of bending it, the round-faced fuller is the tool that is used
—never the keen chisel.   The edge of the set hammer is also usually a little rounding, and does not

form a sharp angle. The same applies also to most of the swages and other tools employed in working out forged forms.

The following figures illustrate in detail these remarks: The crank, Fig. 92, is forged as a solid block, and slotted out at c, whilst the one shown in Fig. 93 is bent round or dipped. When the crank (Fig. 92) is slotted out, the crank webs, a, a, are weak, because the grain or fiber runs in the direction of the engraved lines, and the condition is quite

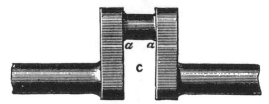

Fig. 92.—Slotted Crank.

Fig. 93.—Bent Crank.

analogous to the short grain in wood. In Fig. 93 the fiber follows the contour of the dip of the crank, and therefore the crank is of equal sectional strength throughout. The weakness of the form, Fig. 92, is shown very forcibly in locomotive practice. The cranks of inside cylinder engines are made in this manner, and unavoidably so, because there is not room enough to use a bent crank like Fig. 93; these cranks invariably fracture at one of the webs (a) when the engine has had a total run of about 200,000

miles. Frequently the webs break before that limit
is reached, and for this reason the practice of bond-
ing is now often resorted to. The crane lifting-hook,
Fig. 94, is invariably bent round like the dip crank,
and its sectional strength is preserved. If it were
slotted the hook would break with much less strain.

Instead of drilling a hole for the eye, *b*, of this
crane-hook, it should be bent round and welded, or
else punched. In drilling, the metal is severed; in

Fig. 94.—Crane Lifting-hook.

punching, it is thrust aside and not divided. The
punching preserves the continuity of the fibers, and,
by bulging out the metal upon each side, preserves
an equal section, and little or no jumping up is required. The punched rod (Fig. 95) is an illustration
of the same kind occurring in the middle of a bar,
and is common in roof trusses.

The eyes of hammers, and the cottar ways in
bolts and rods, should always be punched. There is

then no separation, but only a parting or spreading of the fibers.

In forging the eye of a winch handle (Fig. 96), instead of making a solid end and drilling and filing a square hole, the bar is bent round a mandrel and then welded.

Figs. 97, 98 and 99 show how the continuity of fiber is preserved in large forked ends. Small ends

Fig. 95.—Punched Tie Rod.

Fig. 96.—Welded Eye.

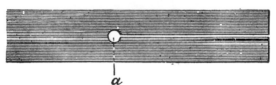

a

Fig. 97.—Bar divided with Hot Set.

are usually shaped out of the solid but broad ends, like that illustrated, and also those of moderate width are formed by dividing the bar and then opening it out. Fig. 97 shows the bar from which the forked end has to be made. A hole is punched through at *a*; this does not sever the fiber, but merely thrusts it sideways. Then the bar is divided with a hot set from the hole *a* outward to the end.

The set is driven first from one face half-way through the bar, and then from the other face to meet in the middle. The punched hole prevents all risk of

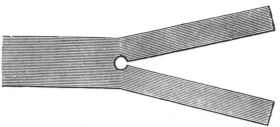

Fig. 98.—Bar opened Out.

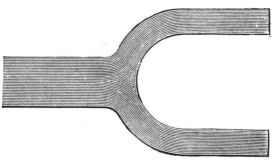

Fig. 99.—Finished Fork End.

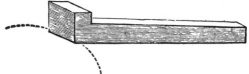

Fig. 100.—Key with Fiber Incorrect.

the set splitting the fibers inwards beyond the hole. Then the bar is opened out, first with a wedge, afterwards with the hammer, as in Fig. 98, and finally finished as at Fig. 99. If the fork were cut from the solid, the fiber would be short; but being opened out and bent round, it runs continuously.

The direction in which the layers of iron occur has frequently to be considered when making forgings. In a cottar key, for example, the layers of iron should be arranged, not in the direction of rota-

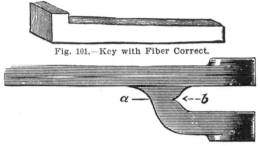

Fig. 101.—Key with Fiber Correct.

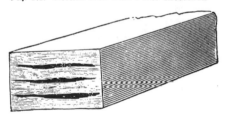

Fig. 102.—Forked End with Fiber Incorrect.

Fig. 103.—Cracks in Bad Iron.

tion of the shaft as in Fig. 100, as the pressure would tend to shear the key off in the plane of the layers, but at right angles, as in Fig. 101, that is, the layers should radiate the center of the shaft, so that the pressure will tend to close them. Nuts should be punched at right angles to the direction of the fiber, otherwise the layers of iron are liable to become separated. The forked eccentric rod end (**Fig. 102**), forged solid and slotted out, should have the layers run not as engraved, but in the plane of the paper instead, otherwise the fiber is apt to open at *b*, and the forked end may fracture along *a, b*.

Liability to crack is much greater in inferior iron than in that of first-class quality. It is not unusual when cut off with the hot set to find the bad qualities of iron showing cracks at the end (Fig. 103). These cracks are due to imperfect union, and to the presence of cinder, which has become intermixed with the iron and not expelled during the process of shingling. Sometimes hammering at a welding heat will improve such iron, but if the composition of the iron is bad, there is little advantage to be gained by this.

Anything that has to be screwed or subjected to great stress or wear, should be forged as sound and close-grained as possible by consolidation under the hammer, or between top and bottom tools at a welding heat. Otherwise the fibers may become partly separated and the metal frayed, so that the open texture of the iron will collect grit and wear rapidly.

CHAPTER VI.

BENDING AND RING MAKING.

This chapter will deal with some of the various methods employed in bending iron and in forming rings in that metal. Curves and rings of light section are easily bent over the beak of the anvil, or around a mandrel of suitable diameter. When the sections are heavy, bending blocks are necessary. It is easier to bend bar-iron flatwise than edgewise; the reason is apparent if it is remembered that when a wide bar is bent two things happen. Along the center of the bar (A, A, Fig. 104) there will be a neutral axis of metal

Fig. 104.—Diagram to Illustrate Tension and Compression.

that bends without compression or extension of fiber. But outside this neutral axis, the metal, B, B, is extended, and inside of this axis the metal, C, C, is compressed. The metal in tension and the metal in compression will seek relief from the intense stresses to which it is subjected. It will become wrinkled and puckered upwards and downwards. This tendency has to be corrected by hammering, or by the use of mechanical devices.

Many devices are resorted to in bending work of various sections and outlines. The making of a special cast iron templet, or bending block, is a question of relative cost. Where only a few plain pieces have to be bent, it will not pay to make the simplest block.

Where there are many pieces, all alike, it pays to cast most elaborate blocks, and to fit them up with clips and cottars, or whatever may be necessary besides. It is usually easy for the smith to design blocks for forgings which he may require.

Fig. 105 shows a common type of block used for

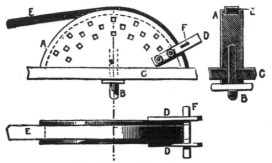

Fig. 105.—Bending Block.

bending flat bars. Made in suitable sections, it is also often employed for bending T-iron. As shown, the working edge, A, is a circular arc; but it could be shaped to other curves equally well. The block has cast in it a stout cottared pin, projecting from its bottom face. This pin passes through a suitable hole in the levelling block, c, and is cottared beneath. For holding down cast-iron templet blocks, this is the most convenient method—better than having movable clips. One end, E, of the bar to be bent, is confined in its groove by clips, D, D. They are fastened with bolts through some of the holes, many of which are usually cast in all bending blocks, the cottar, F, passing through slot holes in D, D, holds the bar, E, down in its groove. As the free end of the bar, E, is bent farther round, more clips are brought to bear upon it, otherwise the bar could rise up from its seating.

Fig. 106 shows a common levelling and bending block fitted with a screw for general work. Upon it bars and plates of metal can be straightened and levelled by hammering. Forgings in process of formation can be tested from its face by the try-square, the back of it being laid upon the block and the blade

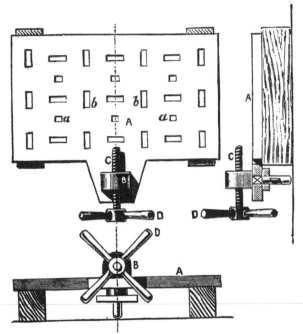

Fig. 106.—Levelling Block with Screw.

against the vertical face of the work to be squared. The bevel gauge can be similarly used. Work can also be taken out of winding upon its surface; and it is used largely for bending iron bars to various curves. The block, A. is pierced with numerous circular and slotted holes, which receive pins forming the necessary supports for leverage when bending. There should be plenty of holes, but the plate should not be unduly weakened. At B there is a screwed

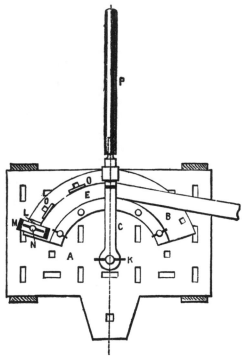

Fig. 107.—Front View of Levelling Block with Bending Templet.

block, secured to the plate with a shank or pin through which a cottar way passes. Driving in the cottar underneath secures this block in position, and by the interposition or removal of a ring the height of the block can be varied. Through the block passes the powerful square-threaded screw, C, which is operated by the heavy cross handle, D. It is evident that

if pins be inserted in holes, say at *a, a,* or at *b, b,* they will afford points of resistance to a bar that is laid against them when pressure is brought to bear about its central portions by the screw, C. As the ends of the bar cannot yield, it will be bent. By shifting the pins into other holes, the curvature of the bar can be varied.

Figs. 107 and 108 illustrate another method of making a ring upon the bending block, shown in Fig. 106. A is the block; B is a templet casting, cottared down to the levelling block through the rough holes cast in the templet, the pins passing through any of the holes cast in the bending block that happen to be conveniently situated. The block is set so that its curvature follows round some particular hole in the bending block, in order that the radius bar or lever C, with its roller, D, may operate with equal pressure upon the ring, E, in every position. The lever moves upon a substantial pivot,

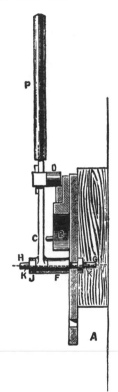

Fig. 108.—Side View of Levelling Block with Bending Templet.

F, whose shank or pin passes through the plate, and is cottared below. The detail of this fitting is shown in Fig. 109, where F is the solid body of the shank,

whose pin, G, passes through the bending block, A.
H is the pin upon which the bar, C, pivots, and J is
a collar, of which one or more may be used for
adjusting the height. K, K are top and bottom
cottars.

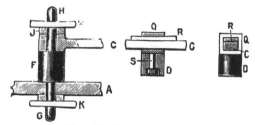

Fig. 109.—Details of Lever.

One end of the bar, E (Figs. 107 and 108), to be
bent is heated, and then secured at one end of the
curved templet. As these templets are made specially
to suit each job, and not for general work, it is
usually practicable to cast a stop at the end where
the bar is first secured. Such a stop is shown at L,
Figs. 107 and 108, and in detail at Fig. 110.

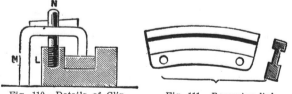

Fig. 110.—Details of Clip.   Fig. 111.—Reversing-link.

This particular templet represents one used for
making rings from which to cut the reversing links,
of the type shown in Fig. 111, of the motion work of
engines. Where such links are made in quantities,
this is a cheaper method than forging and filing or
machining each link separately. Making a ring with

radius equal to the curvature of the link, it is turned all over in the lathe, and then the separate links are slotted out of this ring, all being exactly alike.

In such a case as this, a flat oblong stop, L., Figs. 107 and 108, cast on one end of the templet block, is suitable. When bending a rigid bar, it is very difficult to get the extreme ends sufficiently curved. In this case the stop holds the end perfectly fast, and the curvature can be commenced from the very end. To prevent that end from rising during the process of bending, the clip, M (shown in detail at Fig. 110), is made to bear upon it. This is a piece of stout wrought iron pierced with a hole for the cottared pin, N, screwed into the bending templet. The long leg of the clip rests upon the face of the bending block; the short leg is pressed upon the bar to be bent by the cottar; the bar is thus pinched at one end.

The opposite end, if heavy, is supported by one of those appliances illustrated and described in Chapter I. A man, or two or three men if need be, stands at that end, and by main force pulls the bar round the curved templet, the supporting rest being moved along with the bar. The tendency of the bar to crumple up when the bending is taking place, is corrected by sledge hammer blows. Also to prevent the bar from becoming unequally curved, pins are inserted at intervals in holes cast in the plate, and iron wedges, o (Figs. 107 and 108), are driven between these pins and the bar.

Much force is required to pull round the roller, D, against the edge of the iron. To avoid having a long lever which might be in the way, a bar, P, is often slipped over the end of the radius bar, C, and removed when not in actual use. The mechanism of the roller, D, is shown in detail in Fig. 109. Along the bar slides a block, Q, which may be fixed at any radius with the wedge, R. A stout bolt, S, is screwed

into or forged on this block, and the roller, D, slips
over it, and is held up by the nut underneath.

A heat cannot be taken over a great length in an
ordinary forge fire. Therefore, after a short length,
say from twelve to fifteen inches, of a bar is bent, it
has to be released from the templet and put back into
the fire to get the next section hot; and so on, until
the entire ring is complete. Each time it is put back
on the block, the portion already curved is secured
with wedges. Sometimes also clips like M (Fig. 110)
are cottared down over the bar to prevent it from
rising.

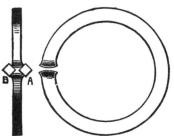

Fig. 112.—Method of Welding Ring.

When the circle is completed the ends have to be
welded. The ends of the ring are upset before being
brought together, and are spread in all directions.
These upset edges are not welded together, but are
united by "stick in" pieces. Into the V-like space
formed on one side by the abutting ends, a square
bar of iron, A (Fig. 112), is laid, and all being
brought to the welding heat, a few blows of the hammer serve to unite the bar and the ends of the ring.
Any length of bar that happens to be handy is taken,
and it is not at first cut off to the length required.
One end only is brought to a welding heat, the opposite cold end serving as a porter. After the welding
is completed, the end is cut off with the hot set.

The ring is then turned over, and a similar "stick in" piece, B, is welded into the opposite V, precisely in the same fashion. The surfaces and edges are very rough and uneven; but the essential work is accomplished, and the rest is merely a matter of battering the faces with the flatter, and trimming the edges with the hot set and flatter. A heavy ring such as this cannot be manipulated easily until the smith's hands are relieved of its dead weight, so one of the appliances illustrated and described in Chapter I. is used.

If a ring, or segment of a ring, is wanted only a few inches larger than the ring, B (Figs. 107 and 108), for which the templet was made, the smith, to save the expense of a new block, will make a filling-up piece (Fig. 113) of square bar.

Fig. 113.—Iron Segment for Increasing Radial Capacity of Templet.

Fig. 114 shows a block of a type useful when a large number of complete rings of the same size are required. The principle of its construction is very similar to that rigged up on the levelling block (Figs. 107 and 108); but in this case a complete circular disc, A, instead of a segment, is used. A lever, B, is pivoted in the center of this disc by means of a cottar and pin, c, or a bolt. A roller, D, is pivoted on this lever. The ring is bent round the annular rebate, *a*, in the disc, and the roller, being pulled round with the lever, is pressed against the edge of the ring, which, confined between the roller, D, and the edge of a rebate on the disc, as shown by shading at *b*, cannot fail to become circular. The ring will have to be held down with clips, as in the previous example, for which purpose the holes cast in the central part of the disc are utilized in the way already described.

A templet like this can also be used for rings slightly larger in diameter and of different widths, by placing rings around the central portion, *a*, of the rebate, and by altering the diameter of the roller, *b*. It is, of course, not necessary that the periphery of

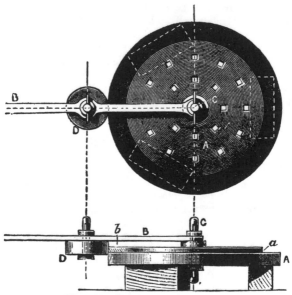

Fig. 114.—Circular Bending Block.

the roller should coincide with that of the disc. If the ring to be formed is larger than the outside of the disc, then the roller will be correspondingly smaller. If the ring is smaller than the disc, then the bottom of the roller will touch on the bottom of the rebated portion.

Slide-valve spindles of the bridle form are made in

two or three ways. The bridle is sometimes circular, sometimes rectangular in shape, but the principle of its formation is the same. In the circular form the eye may be bent round and welded as a distinct ring, and the stem then welded to the eye; by another method a portion only of the eye may be formed, and welded to another portion already made in one with a portion of the stem; by a third method the eye may be turned round and welded from the bar which forms the stem.

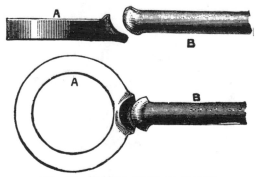

Fig. 115.—Welding Bridle to Spindle.

Fig. 115 illustrates the first method. Here A is the ring which has been upset, and scarfed, bent round on the anvil beak, welded and fullered to receive the upset and fullered stem B, placed in position for welding. The bar-iron from which the bridle, A, is made, is somewhat larger than the finished section—say ⅛ in. each way—and the ring is first bent round to a diameter smaller than that of the finished ring. This allows some finishing work to be done upon the bridle with fullers and flatter, which will have the effect of reducing the area and increasing the diameter. In this way the diameter of the ring may be increased to any reasonable extent, but it could not be reduced.

The ring is slipped over the anvil beak and its truth corrected with the hammer, or over a sugar-loaf-shaped casting (Fig. 114), flatters, fullers, and swages being employed for finally finishing the various flat and curved surfaces.

The bending of large bridles is best done in the manner shown in Fig. 116, and the same method is

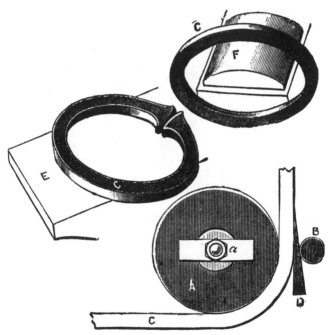

Fig. 116.—Method of Making Rings.

applicable to bending large rings in general. A cast-iron disc, A, of suitable size, and having a central hole, is bolted down on the face of a swage-block, the bolt *a* passing through one of the holes in the block. At a suitable distance a stop or pin, B, is inserted in another of the holes. The bar, C, to be bent is heated and placed between the disc A and the stop B, and is held securely with an iron wedge, D; the free end is pulled round by hand if of sufficient length, or with tongs if short, and struck with the hammer the while to cause close bedding of the iron to the disc. When the ends of the intended ring overlap by an inch or two, it is removed, and the ends are scarfed and upset with the hammer or fullering tool, then welded upon the flat face of the anvil, E (Fig. 116), and finished upon a curved bolster, F. laid upon the anvil face, or provided with a shank to fit into the square hole in the anvil.

An alternative method (Fig. 117) of making the

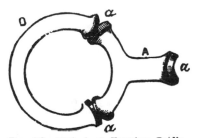

Fig. 117.—Method of Forming Bridle.

valve rod bridle is to take a rod of larger section than the valve rod, and fork one end by punching a hole and then driving in the hot set, first from one face, then from the opposite face, until the nicks meet in the center of the bar. Open out the divided ends into a curved form, and reduce slightly, so as to approximate to the finished dimensions, leaving the ends a (Fig. 117) of the original dimensions, and fullering them diagonally for scarfing (see A), which shows the T-piece finished for welding. The iron, B. that is to form the remainder of the ring,

will be curved, and fullered, and scarfed at the ends
to match the T-piece, A.

At this stage the ring will be less than the finished

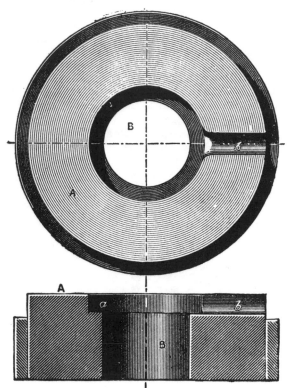

Fig. 118.—Die Block.

diameter—say by about ½ inch, dependent on the
bulk of the work—to allow for working and finishing
subsequent to welding, which stretches the iron. The
spindle will be welded with a scarfed joint on to the

free end *a*, or if the spindle is short it may be drawn
down from the T-piece itself.

Where many bridles are made alike for standard
engines, a die block is employed for final finishing.
Its shape is shown at Fig. 118. A is of cast iron,
cored or bored out at *a* for the bridle, and cored out
at *b* for the stem to lie in; B is a central steel plug
or pin, the size of the hole in the bridle. The bridle
is hammered into the die with a couple of blows of
the steam hammer, next the die is turned upside
down on a suitable bolster, and the pin B and the
forging struck out at a blow. Then the pin is released from the forging, and the bridle is finished,
except for cutting off with a set the fins around the
top edges.

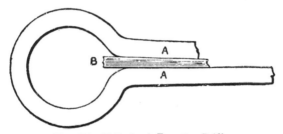

Fig. 119.—Method of Forming Bridle.

Fig. 119 shows the third method, in which the bar
is bent round and welded at A. To preserve the
continuity of the circle, a glut or wedge-piece, B, is
inserted in the weld. Without this, by this method
it would be difficult or impossible to form a perfect
internal curve. The finishing of the bridle by means
of tools and of dies, differs in no respect from that of
the previous example.

The mode of making a rectangular bridle, unless
of small dimensions, would be that shown in Fig.
120. Two T-pieces, A, A, are formed by division simi-

larly to the T-piece A in Fig. 117, and the remainder
of the rectangle is formed of the two pieces, B, B,
bent round and scarfed to meet the scarfed ends of
the T-pieces. The rods may be drawn down from the
ends of A, A, or welded on.

When a smith wants bending blocks of the kind
mentioned in this chapter, it is as well to know that

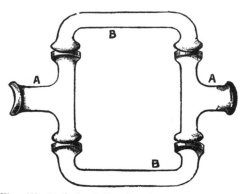

Fig. 120.—Method of Forming Rectangular Bridle.

complete wooden patterns are seldom made for them.
A pattern segment of the block given to the iron-
moulder, with a sketch or drawing of the complete
block, with suitable instructions, is all that is required. The moulder will place any number of plain
cores in the mould for the pin-holes.

CHAPTER VII.

The subjects now to be treated will embrace some
of the common types of forgings, such as rods, levers,
and bolts, made and used in the construction of machinery. Rods and links with bosses, like Fig. 121,

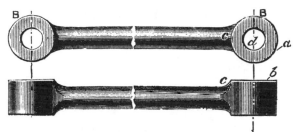

Fig. 121.—Rod or Link with Bosses.

are used extensively in various forms and proportions. At first sight, upsetting would appear to be
the most ready method of making such rods. It
seems simple to take a rod or bar, as the case may
be, the size of the intermediate portion A and to
dump up the ends to make the bosses B. But upsetting tends to open or spread the grain and to impair
its continuity, and the operation would require several heats, and occupy much time, unless the bosses
were very small.

There are three types at least:—(1) When the
bosses are small relatively to their rods, and the rods
are only a few inches long, as in some machinery
links and levers, it is practicable, though not de-

sirable, to form them wholly by upsetting. Properly, they should be made either by partial upsetting and partial drawing down, or wholly by drawing down, according to the stock that happens to be used. (2) When the bosses are relatively large and the eyes relatively small (Fig. 122) and the rods are several

Fig. 122.—Small Tie Rod.

feet in length, as in the tie rods of roofs, they may be forged from the solid, apart from their rods, and welded on. (3) When the eyes are large (Fig. 123),

Fig. 123.—Large Tie Rod.

as in the truss and tie rods of bridges, jibs of travelling cranes, etc., they may be formed by bending round and welding the iron, and usually also by welding the eyes to their rods.

All these will be finished after rough hammering by the aid of the hollow top and bottom tools or swages, operating on the curved edges (*a*, Fig. 121): by the flatter and sledge on the flat faces *b*, and by the fullering tool around the neck *c*. In repetition work the eyes would be finished in a pair of cast-iron

dies, like Figs. 124 and 125; the former gives the
finished curvature to the edges *a* and the fullered
neck *c*, whilst the latter completes the flat faces *b* in
succession. The eye *d* is punched while the boss B
lies in the die, the core falling down into the hole A,
a trifle larger than the punch. The boss is beaten
into the dies with the sledge, or preferably under the
drop, or the steam hammer.

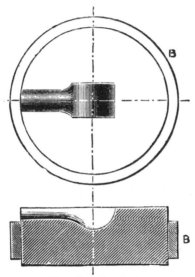

Fig. 124.—Die Block

These blocks are made of square as well as of circular form, but the latter is to be preferred, because
of the greater ease experienced in fitting and shrinking on the bond shown in Figs. 124 and 125, where
B is a wrought-iron bond shrunk on to prevent the
cast iron from bursting from the concussion to which
it is subject.

Dies like this are often made in pairs, top and bottom being coupled with pins for use under the steam hammer.

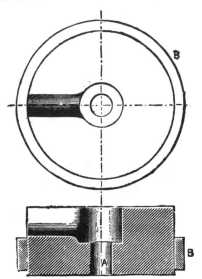

Fig. 125.—Die Block.

(2) The bosses are made from bar iron of their own dimensions, and a sufficient length is drawn down—say from three to six inches—to permit of

Fig. 126.—Boss End Scarfed for Welding.

making, with the long plain body of the rod, a scarfed welding joint (Fig. 126).

(3) The eye is bent round and welded, forming a short solid shank, which is then scarfed and fullered for welding, like Fig. 127.   Or it is bent round to

Fig. 127.—Eye bent for Welding.

form a tongued joint (Fig. 128), in which a wedge-like end is fitted into a corresponding cleft, and

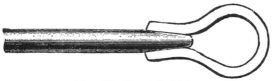

Fig. 128.—Tongued Joint.

welded. This is supposed to be stronger than the plain scarf, and is often used for iron of heavy section.

Fig. 129 shows a tongue joint in solid bars.   To

Fig. 129.—Solid Tongued Joint.

make it, first upset both ends; then for the tongue A set in a fullering tool on opposite sides of the upset portion (Fig. 130, *a*).   Then, by hammering, the end will be tapered down until it has the appearance of Fig. 129, A.   For the recess B, nick the other upset end inwards with a chisel, and open out sufficiently with a wedge. This will spread the end more, as well as open it out; and this spreading out is an advantage, because it gives plenty of metal for welding and swaging down to finished dimensions. The tongue joint is then made in the usual way by heating both ends to the welding heat, and when assured that the faces are free from dirt and scale, closing them together, first with the hammer, and finishing them

Fig. 130.—Fullered End.

with the top and bottom swages. To ensure union at the termination of the tongue, the first blows should be given endwise. These may be given while the work is in the fire, provided the fire is clean, and the joint cleansed by throwing sand into the fire over the work. When the circumference of the joint is being hammered, the angular swages may be used to better advantage than by merely laying the work upon the anvil.

Levers of the general form shown in Fig. 131, but

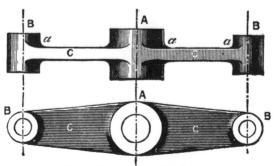

Fig. 131.—Double-ended Lever.

variously proportioned, are very common. The methods of forging them will be modified by circumstances. They may be drawn wholly from the solid, or partly drawn and partly welded—seldom, however, being upset.

A lever of the proportions shown in Fig. 131 would, in general, be formed wholly by drawing down. A bar of iron, having a sectional area about equal to that of the central boss A, is selected. First, a fuller is driven in on opposite sides, as at *a, a, a, a* (Fig. 132). Then the bar is drawn down roughly from the fuller nicks to the ends, until the ends are reduced to an area A (Fig. 132), suitable for the smaller end boss B (Fig. 131). Again the fuller is driven in at

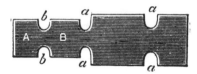

Fig. 132.—Fullered Lump.

b, b (Fig. 132), and then the intermediate portion B is reduced by fullering or by hammering until the required thickness of the web (c in Fig. 131) is nearly reached. The blows are delivered on sides and faces alternately, drawing the sides to the tapered form seen in the plan view, as well as the webs to thickness.

There is no attempt at finish just yet, for the centers of the bosses are probably not the correct size, and it will very likely happen that some further drawing down, or even some upsetting, will be required before the boss lumps will be sufficiently near to correct centers, to permit of their finishing to the required dimensions Rough measurement will be taken from time to time with the rule, or with some form of gauge.

At this stage the lever will resemble Fig. 133, with square lumps at center and ends of the webbed portion. To hammer these bosses into a circular form

Fig. 133.—Lever Roughly Forged.

would involve much labor and several heats, so the corners are cut off with a hot set, as shown by the dotted lines. When a boss is small, four corners only are cut off; when large. eight, or even more.

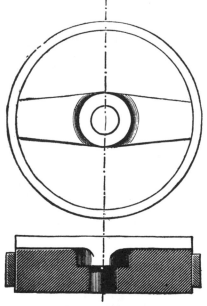

Fig. 134.—Die Block.

The set is driven perpendicularly first, but not right down to the web, it stops at the radius or hollow— and then horizontal cuts are made to meet the perpendicular ones, and so the boss is rudely chiselled to a circular form. Then the hammer, and afterwards the hollow swage, are used to give a more circular

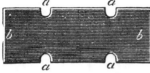

Fig. 135.—Fullered Lump.

Fig. 137.—Boss Lump prepared for Dabbing On.

form to the bosses; and the hollows shown at *a*, *a*. in Fig. 131, are shaped with a hollow fuller. Thus bosses can be made fairly shaped, but not perfectly true. In repetition work dies are used; that for the end bosses would be like Fig. 125, and these (B in

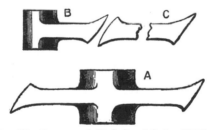

Fig. 136.—Bosses and Rod Scarfed for Welding.

Fig. 131) would be hammered into a recess in the middle of the die, and the web would rest in a recess reaching from the center to the outside. The die for the center boss is shaped like Fig. 134. Bosses finished thus are so true that they can be left without subsequent turning, brightening on the emery wheel giving sufficient finish.

For a lever anything over a foot in length, it

would be easier to take separate pieces of bar iron for
the web, and separate pieces for the bosses, and weld
them together. Thus a lump (Fig. 135) would be
taken for the central boss, and set in with the fuller
at a, a, and drawn down at each end, b, b, leaving the
extreme ends rather thicker than the intermediate
portion, A, Fig. 136, in order to rorm scarfed joints
for welding. The end bosses, B, would be similarly
prepared, and all welded to the webs, c, which is also
upset and scarfed. The shaping and finishing of the
bosses are most conveniently done before the welding
up.

Another way is to weld or "dab" bosses on the
web; these are cut off an iron rod of suitable
diameter. The red-hot boss (Fig. 137) is roughed

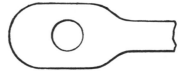

Fig. 138.—Tie Rod End.

with a corner of the chisel, which is held diagonally
and struck with a hammer. These roughings assist
the union of the welded surfaces, which being then
raised to a welding heat, the flat bars and the bosses
are made to adhere by a few hammer blows. The
thinner the web, the more intimate and secure the
weld.

When forging articles in this way, it will be necessary to test the parallelism and the rectangular form,
and the winding of the various parts. Forgings are
apt to develop inaccuracy quickly while the metal is
soft, so the smith employs the eye in these early
stages of the work, and squares, and calipers, and
straight-edges as it becomes cooler.

Large tie-rod ends (Fig. 138) are always welded to
their rods. A rectangular lump is drawn down (Fig.

139) at the end A to a trifle larger than the rod, and scarfed for welding. The corners B are rounded by first cutting off the angles with the hot set, and then by rounding off with the chisel shown at Fig. 145.

Fig. 139.—Rough Forging for Tie Rod End.

In these rods the eyes, being large, are usually punched first, and frequently they are reamered out afterwards. Such large holes are punched with difficulty under the sledge, but easily under the steam hammer. Fig. 140 shows the arrangement employed:

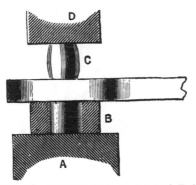

Fig. 140.—Punching Hole in Tie Rod End.

A is the anvil of the steam hammer, and upon this rests the bolster, B, which must be sufficiently large to give proper bearing support to the eye, and its hole must be a trifle larger, but not much larger than that of the punch c. Two or three blows of the hammer or tup, D, will drive the punch through; this is

slightly bellied in order to squeeze the metal, and also
to clear itself of the hole easily.

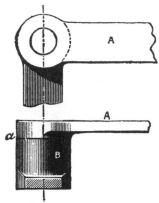

Fig. 141.—Lever Arms.

After rounding the edges and punching the hole,
but before the bar is quite cool, the flatter will be
used to smooth over the edges that have been slightly
upset during these processes.

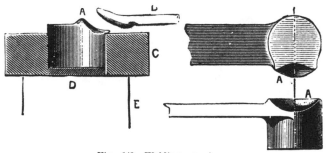

Fig. 142.—Welding on Arm.

Often the arms of bossed levers stand at an angle
with each other, and also are not in the same plane,
and then the methods previously described are not

applicable. Fig. 141 shows a portion of a lever, with arms placed on opposite sides of the boss at right angles to each other. There are two ways in which these levers may be attached to the boss. One by "dabbing on"—that is, the arm A, with a portion of the boss, is welded flat upon the main portion of the boss B, along the plane *a*, the surfaces being first hatched over with the corner of a set; by the other way (Fig. 142), one side of the boss, if fullered, as at

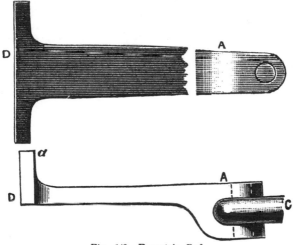

Fig. 143.—Eccentric Rod.

A, with a round-faced fuller, the end of the lever arm B is upset, and the two welded together. This is a very common method of welding. The fuller not only indents the boss, but, by means of blows delivered diagonally, is made to throw up the metal all around in a ridge, thus giving some extra metal for finishing off. In Fig. 142, c is a die-block, in which the boss is held while the arm is being welded; D is a thickness piece, or washer; and E is the anvil. If no

die-block is available, the boss will be held with
open-mouthed tongs of globular form.

Eccentric and valve rods afford some typical examples of engine forgings. The eccentric rod (Fig.
143) is usually made in two pieces, and welded at
about the center; or, if rather long, the ends are
welded to a central plain bar.

The extreme dimensions of the end A represent
roughly the original size of the bar, from which the
shank B is drawn down. From that original bar
there is swaged down a length sufficient for welding.
The large end is cut off to the precise length required
with the knife tool, or with the curved knife if the
steam hammer is used, or with a hot set if power is
not available. Then it is necessary to cut off upon
the anvil any sharp corners with a cutting-off tool,
giving the appearance of Fig. 144, and swage the end

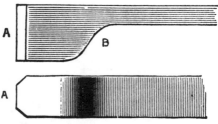

Fig. 144.—Forked End Roughed Out.

A, rounding with a hollow swage, letting the shoulder
B lay against the beak of the anvil, and finally, to
finish in a die-block (Fig. 145). Of course, the die-
block is used for finishing only when the quantity
of forgings required is sufficient to pay for its cost.

The body A of the block is of cast iron, and a
wrought iron ring B is shrunk on. The recess C, it
will be seen, corresponds with the outline of the end
A in Fig. 143.

Another way to forge the forked end is to take a bar about half the thickness of the forked end, and double the iron over, and weld a length that will extend rather farther than the termination of the radius.

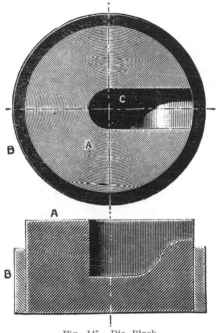

Fig. 145.—Die Block.

In both of these methods the gap may be cut out roughly by the smith or left to be machined out. The general methods of forming forked ends have already been described, and now it is only necessary to show by a sketch how forked ends, whose gaps are formed by forging, and not by machinery, are shaped. After

the metal has been cut out from the gap and roughly
brought to form, a filler, shown shaded at c, Fig. 143,
is inserted, and while this remains in, the outside of
the forked end is finished with flatter and hollow
swage. The filler usually has a square shank to fit
the square hole in the anvil.

The end D in Fig. 143 is made by one of three
methods. Either the shank B is fullered down from a
bar of the original section of the end D; or the shank
A (Fig. 146) is welded to a piece of flat bar B, of the

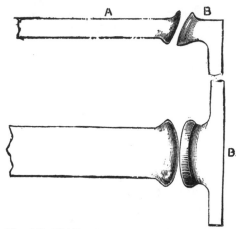

Fig. 146.—Welding Flat End of Eccentric Rod.

dimensions of the end D in Fig. 143; or the end of a
bar is divided and opened out. The first method is
not correct because the iron fibers are short, but it
is often adopted, as there is not very much stress on
the flat end when bolted up to the eccentric straps,
and the hammering it receives at the welding heat
helps to consolidate the metal.

The second method has the advantage of preserving
the best arrangement of the fibers. In it, the flat

piece B (Fig. 146) is fullered and upset with a round-
faced fuller, and the end A, similarly fullered, is
welded to it. In either case, to permit of finishing
off, the iron selected is a trifle larger in section than

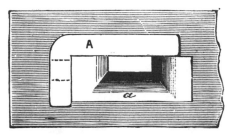

Fig. 147.—Anvil Stop.

the finished section. Where the shank is drawn down
from the solid, a good deal of finish on face *a* (Fig.
143) has to be done with the flatter, the rod being
held vertically with the face D upon the anvil face.
To prevent the rebounding backwards of the forging,
in consequence of the edge of the flatter striking the

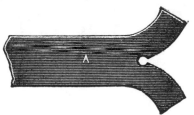

Fig. 148.—Opening Out End of Bar.

shank, a bent bar of iron (Fig. 147, A) is fitted with
a shank into the hole on the anvil face. The flatting
of the inner face *a* of course has a tendency to spread
the edges and bulge them in some places, and this is
corrected with blows on those edges from the hammer
and from the flatter.

The third method of forming the flat end is by forking the end of a stout bar in the fashion shown in Fig. 148, and opening the ends outwards. Continuity of fiber is thus preserved. The end A is fullered down thinner, and drawn out, and then cut off

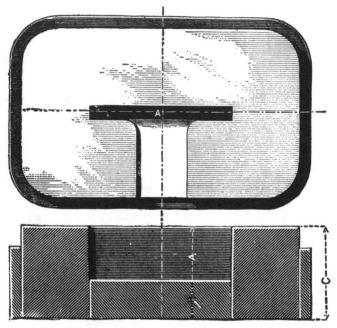

Fig. 149.—Die Block.

the main bar, whose length may serve as a porter, and scarfed for welding to the stem.

When these rods are made in quantities, the final finish is imparted in a cast-iron die of the form shown in Fig. 149, in which A is the recess that gives the flat end its perfect finish, and B a flat piece of steel, whose depth makes up the precise difference between the depth c and of the flat end A, and by means of which the T-end is driven out of the die immediately after it is moved off the anvil block of the steam hammer. The block being turned upside down, a blow or two on the piece B drives the finished T-piece out from the die.

When the fins formed at the edges are being cut off with the set, the forging is placed upon a piece of sheet iron, bent over at the ends to clip the edges of the anvil. This sheet of iron prevents the cutting edges of the set from becoming dulled by contact with the hard steel face of the anvil.

Bolts and nuts are bought more cheaply than they can be forged in small quantities, and they are consequently seldom made in smiths' shops. But a de-

Fig. 150.—Ring for Bolt Head.

Fig. 151.—Rod driven into Ring.

scription of their manufacture is not superfluous, because in it are illustrated several facts that find useful application in other classes of work.

In making bolts there is the choice of three methods. In one, a bar is selected of about the size of the bolt head across the angles, and the stem is drawn down, first roughly by the hammer, and then between swages.

Another method is to take a bar of the diameter of the bolt and upset a mass of metal to form the head. Neither of these methods, however, is often adopted.

The usual method is to bend round and weld a ring of metal upon a bar, whose diameter equals that of the bolt. The details are as follows:—The heads are prepared as rings (Fig. 150) cut off from a rectangu-

lar bar of iron, and bent round upon the anvil beak
or upon a mandrel, but not welded as yet. For the
shanks, suitable lengths of round rod are cut off. To
economize time, as many rings and lengths of rod
are prepared as there are bolts wanted, and then the
welding begins. First the end of a rod, made red
hot, is driven through its ring (Fig. 151), which lies
upon the anvil; the rod is next brought into a horizontal position, and the ring closed tightly upon it by
two or three smart blows of the hammer, and also the
end of the rod is slightly burred over with the hammer (Fig. 152) to keep the ring from slipping. That

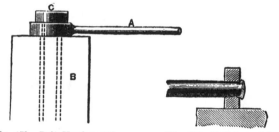

Fig. 153.—Bolt Header and   Fig. 152.—Rod burred in.
Block.

end is then put into the fire and raised to a welding
heat, and sand is sprinkled over it just before withdrawal from the fire. The head is laid in a hexagonal bottom tool (Fig. 54, p. 32), and about half a
dozen blows given to it, altering the position of the
head after each blow. It is then put into a bolt
header A (Fig. 153), resting on a cast iron heading
block B, pierced with a central hole, and the top of
the bolt head, C, is well beaten over with hammer
and flatter. The bolt is then put back in the hexagonal bottom tool (Fig. 54, p. 32) and once more hammered on each separate face; then back in the bolt
header, and struck twice or thrice with a flatter, and
then finished with a cup tool, which gives the round-

ing at the edges. Finally, it is put back in the hexagonal swage, and a last blow given with the flatter on each face. All this is done at a single heat, and, when finished (Fig. 154), the bolt head, unless very small, is still at a good red heat. A description of an appliance used in rounding bolt heads commences on p. 12.

Many bolts, such as those used for glands and for some forms of plummer blocks, are furnished with collars. These are usually welded on as rings, and finished in a die or swage of the form in Fig. 49, p. 31.

To make nuts in small quantities, take a flat iron

Fig. 154.—Finished Bolt Head.

Fig. 155.—Rod Bent to Form Chain Link.

bar of a thickness and width the same as the nuts, and mark off and nick their lengths with a cold chisel. Center-pop the middle of each space. Heat the bar and over a bolster punch all the holes through in succession. Then cut off each nut on the anvil chisel, and finish on a mandrel.

The manufacture of chains is quite a distinct branch, but a smith is often called to mend a broken chain. When a broken link is replaced it is usually made a trifle longer than the normal link, for convenience of formation. Also, when a link is added to one end of a chain for the purpose of connecting it to any attachment—as a crane hook, for example— the link is made slightly longer. Such an added link is termed a shutting link.

To weld a shutting link, the iron rod is first bent to

a U shape (Fig. 155), then two opposite faces, *a*, *b*, are drawn off diagonally with the hammer, and the link is bent round to bring these faces nearly close toge.her (Fig. 156). The link is then put back into

Fig. 156.—Chain Link.

the fire and brought to a welding heat, a little sand strewn upon the joint, which is closed smartly with the hammer, first on the flat upon the anvil, and then upon a tool (Fig. 157) fixed in the hole in the anvil.

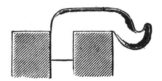

Fig. 157.—Link-forming Tool in Anvil.

To smooth and finish the link a hollow swage tool is worked around it.

Swivels are of common occurrence, and require some art in making. Fig. 158 shows a piece of iron

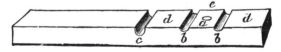

Fig. 158.—Bar Iron for Making Swivel.

bar, the cross section of which should be rather greater than that of the boss of the swivel, because then neither welding on nor upsetting is necessary. A hole is first punched at *a*, corresponding with the eye of the swivel; then a moulding tool (Fig. 159) is laid across the red-hot bar, roughly concentric with the punched hole, *a*, and struck a few blows with the

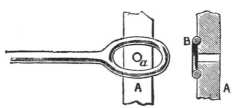

Fig. 159.—Moulding Tool for Swivel.

steam hammer, leaving the impressions *b*, *b* (Fig. 158).

In the absence of a steam hammer, a fullering tool would answer the same purpose as the moulding tool,

Fig. 160.—Boss of Swivel.

but it would take longer time. The moulding tool not only fullers, but imparts the desired curved form to the incipient boss. After fullering, the bar is cut off at *c* (Fig. 158), and the portions *d*, *d*, are drawn

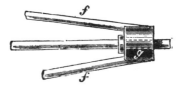

Fig. 161.—Mandrel in Swivel.

down to a sectional area a trifle larger than that of the arched portions of the swivel. At the same time the boss portion is shaped out of the lump *e* until the

forging has the appearance of Fig. 160. Then a mandrel (Fig. 161) is passed through the punched hole, *a*
and the drawn-down ends are hammered over as at
f, f. At the same time the forging, while on the
mandrel, is finished all over, except just where the

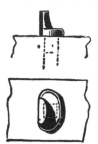

Fig. 162.—Arms of Swivel   Fig. 163.—Bolster Tool for
    Upset for Welding.   Forging Swivel.

weld is to be made, the boss *g* and the arms *f, f*, with
their merging curves, all being gone over in detail
with the hollow tools and fullers. The extreme ends
of the arms *f, f*, are also scarfed and slightly upset,
and the forging then has the appearance of Fig. 162.
To afford support to the swivel during the welding,

Fig. 164.—Finished Swivel.

the beak of the anvil is utilized, or a special bolster
like tool (Fig. 163) is fitted into the hole in the anvil.
The face of this tool is shaped roughly to the curve
of the swivel, and lends itself readily to the work of
welding and finishing with hollow tools, during which

the position of the swivel on its bolster is being continually shifted. The form of the finished swivel is shown at Fig. 164, the scarfed weld being at *h*.

Another way of forming such a swivel is shown in Fig. 165. A round rod, A, is divided and forked, as

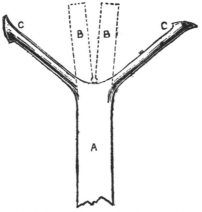

Fig. 165.—Swivel formed from Round Bar.

seen by the dotted lines, B. the divided ends still further opened out and drawn down and upset, as at C, C; after this, the process is similar to that previously explained.

CHAPTER VIII.

CRANKS, MODEL WORK, AND DIE FORGING.

The blacksmith is often called upon to forge cranks and crank axles. These appear in many different forms, so it is impossible to give fully detailed accounts of the methods employed in the construction of all of them. One or two cranks of the more general kind will, therefore, be noticed.

Suppose a common bent or dip crank of round section (Fig. 166) has to be made without assistance

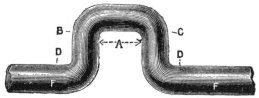

Fig. 166.—Bent Crank.

from a die-block. It would not do simply to bend a round bar to the cranked form, because at the corners where the bending takes place the area would be reduced by the stretching. Bad iron is of no use for a bent crank, for the process of upsetting and bending will open out the fibers; fagoted iron is often used.

A crank of this kind (Fig. 166) may have one, two, or three throws, and the axles extending at each end may be long or short. The cranks may be forged separately, and apart from the axles, and afterwards welded together, or all may be forged from one bar, as is most convenient.

It is supposed that the crank has only one dip; but to a certain extent it is applicable to cranks with two or three dips, the twisting of the dips to relative angles with each other excepted.

Before bending the dips, there will be three upsettings of the iron: one along the length, A, that is to form the future crank pin, and the bendings, reaching from B to C in Fig. 166, where the pin merges into the webs or arms, and two others where the webs are to merge into the axle, or from B to D, and C to D (Fig. 166). These upsettings are done before the bar is bent.

The bendings at B and C will be done either at one or two heats. If the pin is short, one heat will suffice, but if long, two will be necessary. Here the swage block, or the levelling block pierced with numerous holes, is of use; a couple of pins inserted into holes in either block, form suitable supports in pulling the axles round and preserve the true plane of the dip. If neither swage block nor levelling block is available, a pin placed in the anvil hole must answer the same purpose, but it will not be suitable for heavy work.

It is necessary to check the width, A (Fig. 166), before bending the other corners. Upsetting must be resorted to if too great, and drawing down if not enough.

The bending of the corners D, E, can be done around suitable pins, the axles F, F, affording good leverage. After this the crank webs from B to D, and from C to E, must be set parallel, and the axles F, F, set for alignment lengthways, and be brought into the same plane with the webs and pin.

In cranks of this type, it is desirable and usual to have rather an excess of metal at the corners, especially when they are to be finished bright. Such cranks, when made in quantities, are usually bent over a block, or they are stamped.

A bending block is shown in plan and elevation by Fig. 167. A section on A, B, is shown by Fig. 169,

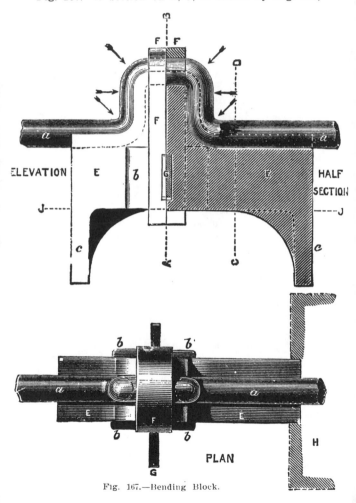

Fig. 167.—Bending Block.

and another on c, d, by Fig. 168. The block is a casting, E, sufficiently heavy to resist the hammer blows necessary for making the bends of the crank. Its width is therefore considerably greater than the diameter of the crank, and ample depth is given. The length is sufficient to permit of true alignment of the axle being made, though not necessarily so great as that of the crank axle. The distances from

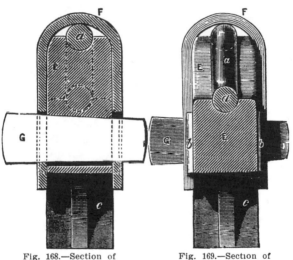

Fig. 168.—Section of
Bending Block.

Fig. 169.—Section of
Bending Block.

the center line A B to each end are made unequal to permit of the forging of cranks with two throws or three throws. For single dip cranks only the lengths would be equal. In Fig. 167 the right-hand end is made sufficiently long to afford a good bedding for the axle *a*, but the left-hand end is made short, so that after one throw is forged it may lie beyond the left-hand end to permit of the bending of the second or the third throw upon the block.

In the formation of a crank by the aid of such a
block, those sections where the bendings are to be
made are thickened by upsetting as before described,
and the webs are bent upon the levelling block or
upon the swage block, and the axles bent at right
angles with the webs approximately true, though not
necessarily so carefully as though the crank were
intended to be finished by this method. The advantage of the block now becomes apparent. The crank
a, heated nearly to a welding heat, is dropped over
the block E, embraced by the strap F, tightened by
the cottar c, which being driven in rapidly holds it
in place, and the webs and the axles are bedded
down into the curved recess of the block, hammer,
fuller, and hollow tools being quickly brought into
requisition wherever wanted. Thus the crank is prac-
tically finished, only a little smoothing over being
done after removal from the block, chiefly at the sides
which cannot be got at while the crank lies on the
block. The crank should be removed from the block
soon, or it will become bound tight, owing to the
shrinkage of the metal by cooling. For this reason
the sides of the block should be tapered slightly,
and for large cranks, when making the block, allowance for shrinkage in cooling should be given at the
rate of about ¼ in. per foot.

In Fig. 167, *b*, *b*, are guide strips cast upon the
sides of the block E for the strap F. If the strap is
not sufficiently stout, a clamp or a rough gib may hold
its bottom ends together. The two horns, c, c, are
cast on for convenience. As the blows for the most
part are delivered in the direction of the arrows, the
block needs to be steadied endwise; therefore, in the
example from which this is taken, a heavy cast-iron
block is sunk into the ground, a little below the shop
floor. It is grooved out at one end to take the parts
c, c, which preserve the bending block steady under
the hammer blows. The grooved end of this casting

is shown dotted at H, Fig. 167; c, c, are below the ground—J J being the level of the floor.

If a second or third dip has to be forged, the truth of the first one is preserved by inserting in the dip a packing block B, Fig. 170, which gives an elevation

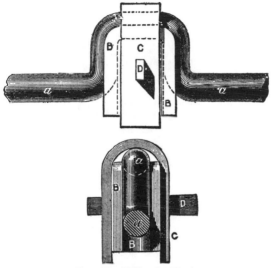

Fig. 170.—Filling-in Block.

and side view. This is a cast-iron piece hollowed semicircularly to fit the webs, and secured in place with a strap, c, and cottar, D. This is retained in place until the remaining dip or dips are bent. Fig. 171 shows a form of crank axle that is well adapted for forging into the strongest form possible, the fiber running round the bent portions. In some other forms the same advantageous disposition of metal is not secured.

Formerly it was quite common to see the largest crank axles of the general form shown in Fig. 172

built up by preparing separately the pin A. the webs B, and the axles C, and welding them together. The webs were opened out at the one end to embrace the pin and at the other end to embrace the axle, and then all welded together. Now it is usual in very large cranks, on marine engines especially, to make

Fig. 171.—Crank roughly fullered into form.

and machine each of these parts separately and weld them together, shrinking the webs on to the pin. In small cranks of this type the forging is made solid and machined out. Briefly, the methods employed are as follows:—The simplest and the worst way is to cut the entire crank out of a slab. Better than

Fig. 172.—Locomotive Type of Crank.

this is the drawing down of the axles from a lump whose width is equal to the total width of the crank from the outer edge of the axle to the outer edge of the pin. Better still is the fullering out of a lump in such a way that an approximately curved disposition of the fibers is obtained (see Fig. 171), leaving, however, a good deal of finishing and machining to be done afterwards.

Another way—not so good as the last, but more common—is to weld on one or several pieces, A, to one side of the bar, B, that is to form the axle (Fig. 173), leaving the gap to be slotted out or drilled out.

In cranks having two and three throws, the gaps stand at angles of 90° and 120° respectively. Cranks like Fig. 166 are usually forged with the dips at proper angles, but those like Fig. 174 are more often forged with the dips in one plane and twisted afterwards. When built, they are sometimes forged approximately at these angles. Sometimes each crank is prepared separately, and welded to suitable lengths

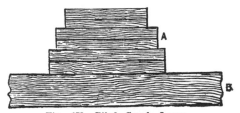

Fig. 173.—Piled Crank Lump.

of axle. When twisting is practiced it must be performed over as great a length of shaft as possible, in order to be gradual. Two or three heats may have to be given if the length is considerable, and a portion of the necessary twist imparted at each heat. One crank will have to be secured by some means, such as clamping down to the swage or levelling block or anvil, or holding under the steam hammer, or in the vice, while leverage is exerted at the other end. The leverage may be applied direct to the other crank, or to the axle itself, by means of clips. A few well-directed blows of the hammer will assist and serve to regulate the dead pull exerted upon the lever. If the cranks are welded to the axle, a long and somewhat bulky scarf should be made, to give plenty of metal for subsequent consolidation and swaging down.

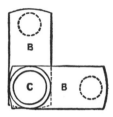

Fig. 174.—Locomotive Type of Crank.

The bosses for some large stationary engine-cranks when they are not upset, or the webs not swaged from the solid, are built up or bent round in various fashions. In one method the boss is formed by bending round a piece of bar *a*, and welding it to a straight portion B (Fig. 175). The bending is usu-

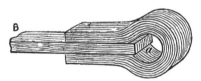

Fig. 175.—Crank Boss.

ally done by placing the bar across two supports, and fullering it down at the central portion. When the bar is thus partly bent, the curving is finished by closing the ends upon the anvil, till they just embrace the flat bar B in readiness for welding; more than one thickness of metal may be employed in the formation of the boss.

To finish such a boss, any excess of metal at the end, *a*, of the bar is cut off with a chisel, a mandrel is then inserted in the hole, and the outer curves finished with fullers.

Often, however, the loss is made simply by piling (Fig. 176). The pieces A, A, of any convenient thickness, are welded to the straight bar B, and afterwards are consolidated at a welding heat; a rudely curved form is imparted to them by means of fullering tools before final shaping with the set and finishing tools.

When the two bosses are prepared, the ends B, which have served as porters, are cut off, and the bosses united by means of a scarfed joint, thus forming a double-ended boss whose middle portion, or web, can be fullered and swaged down to the lesser section required.

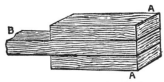

Fig. 176.—Lump for Crank Boss.

When extra strong and sound forgings are wanted, a solid new bar is not used, but a large number of selected pieces of any size and shape are welded together, the operation being known as piling or fagoting. The pieces are laid together in bundles of suitable sizes, bound round with iron to a porter or long bar of iron, and heated and welded and reduced under the steam hammer. For special work this process is repeated two or three times, the pile being drawn down, and then cut off into lengths that are re-piled, and reheated, and welded. The bars are not merely laid in parallel series, but are often made to cross one another at various angles, to secure greater strength. By this means, not only are forgings with the maximum of strength procurable, but all the odds and ends of metal cut off in the processes of forging are utilized.

Forgings for model work are necessarily expensive.

In the first place, in order to produce shapely and accurate forgings, much time must be spent upon them. In the second place, very few smiths care to undertake such work, because ordinary forging pays better, and because a man must execute very neat work to turn out perfect model forgings. Yet it is work that practiced amateurs, with time at their disposal, can succeed fairly well with, because patience more than high skill is wanted, and scarcely any of the really difficult operations of forgings are involved. Few special tools are required, most of the work being done with hammers and files. The cost of material is small, and the principal appliances are a small anvil and a vice.

In touching upon the differences between model and general work, it may be said generally that there is less of welding and more of drawing down done in forgings for model work than in those of heavy type. The difference in the dimensions of bossed-up ends or forked ends and their shanks or rods is so small relatively, that it is much easier to reduce the rods with the hammer than to weld the ends on. There is no great difficulty in welding small work, provided no time is lost in hammering the parts together immediately on removal from the fire.

For very light work, a small combined anvil and vice will probably be found serviceable. One advantage of a small anvil is that the beak is very useful to bend curves, and to form a suitable bedding when fullering down curved necks and shoulders for which the ordinary fullering tools are too large. The cross peens of the hammers are useful for this operation, and with different sizes various curvatures can be formed. Flatters are not used, all the battering and smoothing that is done being effected with the hand hammer.

Owing to the unsuitability of smiths' ordinary finishing tools for purposes of model work, the file has to be used much more largely in this class of work than in ordinary forgings. When the forgings are cooling down to a black heat, a good deal of material can be removed with little effort, and a certain amount of finish imparted.

Again, in small forged work, many parts are left solid that in large work would be punched or fullered or cut out. The holes in bosses would seldom be punched, but wholly drilled. The forked ends of eccentric rods are left to be slotted or filed out.

In wrought iron used for model forgings, the same regard must be had to the direction of the grain as in larger forgings. But, in all respects steel is preferable as a material for model work to wrought iron. It is hard, rigid, and strong—important considerations—takes a better polish, and is more durable.

Die forging, or stamping, is adopted by the smith for repetition work. There are numerous parts in nearly all branches of smiths' work that are required precisely alike, and an enormous saving is effected by the use of dies. Such parts as flat links for chain, flanges for steam and exhaust pipes, some portions of valve gear. ornamental bosses, railing heads, pins, small levers, and similar articles more or less intricate, can be readily stamped with proper appliances.

Large dies are usually made of cast iron, and the smaller of steel. In large dies the required impressions are cast, and afterwards cleaned and smoothed a little with the file; in small dies they have to be cut out with drills, chisels, and files. In either case, sufficient metal must be put into the die to enable it to withstand the concussion of the blows. Cast dies are frequently bonded with a wrought-iron ring, in order to. prevent their bursting. For this kind of work the sledge is of no use, generally the drop hammer, steam hammer, or hydraulic press being used. In little shops unprovided with power, the Oliver often serves.

In the plainest work a single die will often suffice, and the formation of the die must vary with the shapes of the forgings. But if the top of a forging is not flat, then two dies must be used, the upper portion being cut to the requisite outline. The top portion must also be attached to the lower in such a way that it will take its proper position in relation to the lower instantly, without any adjustment. This is usually effected by means of iron dowels, two or three dowels being driven tightly into the lower portion of the die, and standing upwards to fit loosely into corresponding holes drilled in the top portion of the die. The dowels are well tapered, and their ends rounded off so as to go more easily into the holes in the top portion of the die. The bottom dies are sometimes furnished with long handles, or they are lifted about with the hoop tongs, the top dies alone being furnished with handles. When holes have to be punched in the forgings, corresponding holes are usually drilled in top and bottom dies. The top holes are then parallel, and of the same size as the punch which is inserted in them; but the bottom ones are of the same size only where the lower face of the forging lies, being tapered downwards to allow the punched discs to fall through freely.

In many cases two sets of dies are requisite to produce an article; one set will form the sides, and another set the top and bottom. Of course, dies are expensive and, as a general rule, only pay when there are at least several dozens of an article required.

In stamped work, the amount of material required for any given forging must be gauged with accuracy. If there is an excess of metal, there will be thick fins spreading over the edges. If, on the other hand, the metal is short, then the forgings will not come up keen and clean, but will have edges more or less rounding and inaccurate.

CHAPTER IX.

HOME-MADE PORTABLE FORGES.

Illustrations and brief descriptions of some of the better known forges are given in Chapter I., but it is thought that some readers, instead of buying a forge

Fig. 177.—Home-made Portable Forge.

ready-made, may wish to construct one themselves.
Such readers will be interested in the following par-

Fig. 180.—Bracket for Supporting Lever of Portable
Forge.

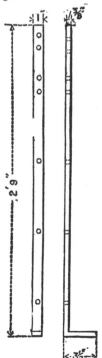

Fig. 178.—Legs of
Portable Forge.

Fig. 179. — Pattern for
Portable Forge Tray.

ticulars of a portable forge which can be easily made by an iron-worker. The appliance (Fig. 177) consists of a wrought-iron frame, on the top of which is the tray, or hearth; and underneath is the bellows and blowing arrangement.

The whole of the framework is made of 1 in. by ⅜ in. square iron bar, and is riveted together by ⅜ in. by ⅞ in. and ⅜ in. by 1¼ in. iron rivets, the holes being bored to allow the rivets to fit in rather tight. The dimensions of the various parts of the framework are all in the illustrations.

The framework consists of four legs, A, A, A, A (Fig. 177), braced together by the cross-stays, B, B, two above and two below the bellows. The two stays above the bellows are not shown in the figure, being hidden by the tray, etc. They are of the same form and dimensions as the bottom pair, except at the center, where they cross each other, one of them being cranked down to allow the other to cross at its own level, and thus make a level bed for the hearth-tray to rest on. One of the legs is shown in front and side elevation in Fig. 178.

The various parts of the framework should first be forged and cut to dimensions given in drawings, and tried to make sure that they are all exact before marking out for drilling. The two cross stays, B, B (Fig. 177), are riveted together where they cross in the center of the frame as shown. The ring, D (Fig. 177), is placed round the outside of frame at the points where the cross-stays are riveted to the legs, and the rivets pass through the ring, D, legs, A, A, A, A, and cross-stays, B, B, binding them all securely together.

The hearth consists of a flat, round plate of iron, sufficiently thick to withstand the heat; it is more serviceable, though a little more expensive, if made of thinner material and a circular fireclay brick bottom is placed on it. The hearth-plate rests on the

top pair of cross-stays, and is riveted to them by four
rivets, two in each stay. The circular band, ɪ, sur-
rounding the hearth is cut out of 3-16 in. sheet iron
to the shape shown at Fig. 179; the hole ᴀ is for the
introduction of the tuyere, ᴊ, from the bellows. The

Fig. 181.—Spindle of Portable Forge.

band is riveted to the top of each leg by two rivets.
as shown at ᴘ, ᴘ (Fig. 177), and is also riveted together at its two ends, as shown at ᴏ, by four rivets.
The hearth-plate is cut to exactly fit inside the band.
ɪ, and to rest on the top pair of cross-stays.

Fig. 182.—End of Spindle of Portable Forge.

Fig. 183.—Crank on
End of Spindle of
Portable Forge.

The bellows work consists of a spindle of ¾-in.
round iron, working in two brackets, shown at ᴋ
(Fig. 177), and in detail by Fig. 180. One of these
brackets is riveted to each of two opposite legs, by
two rivets in each as shown in Fig. 177. The spindle

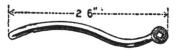

Fig. 184.—Lever on End of Spindle of Portable Forge.

is shown at ʜ (Fig. 177), and also by Fig. 181, the
ends, ǫ, being squared (see Fig. 182) to fit the small
cranks, ʟ, and the long lever, ᴍ (Fig. 177). These

cranks are shown in plan and elevation in Fig. 183, and the long lever in Fig. 184. As will be seen from Fig. 182, the ends of the lever are squared and screwed. The length for the square part is ¾ in.

Fig. 185.—Guide-stay for Bellows of Portable Forge.

This is for the end carrying the long lever, as well as the crank; the other end, which carries only a crank, will have the squared part ½ in. long.

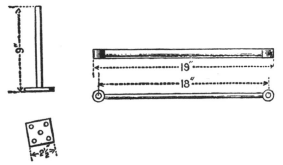

Fig. 186.—Guide-pin for   Fig. 187.—Bellows Links of Portable
Portable Forge Bellows.   Forge.

The cross-stay, c (Fig. 177), acts as a guide to ensure the top chamber of the bellows rising and falling perpendicularly. It is secured to one pair of legs by rivets as the cross-stays are; it is made of 1 in. by ¾ in. iron bar, swelled out and has a hole in the center, as shown at Fig. 185, to allow the guide-rod, F (Fig. 177), to slide easily through. The upright ½-in. round guide-rod and square plate are shown in

Fig. 186. The plate is countersunk to receive four screws, which attach it to the top board of the bellows, the rod being riveted into the plate. The bellows, E (Fig. 177), is fastened to the frame by four

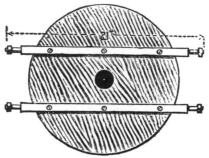

Fig. 188.—Under View of Portable Forge Bellows.

stout wood screws, one through each leg. Between the legs and the center board of bellows are placed four pieces of ½-in. iron pipe, each about 1 in. long; the four screws pass through the legs into these

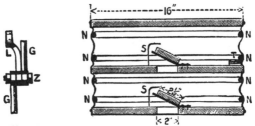

Fig. 189. — Link and Crank Connection of Portable Forge.

Fig. 190.—Section through Portable Forge Bellows.

pieces of pipe, and are driven home into the center-board of bellows, holding them quite securely.

The bottom chamber of the bellows is supported by four links, shown at G, G, G, G (Fig. 177). Each

end of these links is swelled out (see Fig. 187) at
the bottom ends, and has a hole to fit on the round
ends of two flat bars made of 1-in. by ⅜-in. iron bar,
running across the bottom board of bellows (shown
in Fig. 188), and at the top ends for the reception
of the ⅜-in. bolts, which connect them to the short
crank, L (Fig. 177). This arrangement is better seen
at Fig. 189, L being the short crank, G, G the links,
and z the ⅜-in. bolt and nut. The flat bars just men-

Fig. 191.—Nozzle and Bellows Connection of Portable Forge.

tioned are drawn out to a round section at the ends,
and screwed for nuts, which keep the links in their
place. They are fastened to the bottom board of the
bellows by three screws in each passing through holes
drilled and countersunk to receive them.

The bellows is composed of three circular boards of
inch stuff, 14½ in. in diameter. The middle and bottom boards are each provided with a valve, opening
upwards. These are made by drilling a hole, 2 in.

in diameter, in the center of each board. Over each of these holes is placed a flat, circular piece of leather nailed to the board at one side which forms a hinge, but otherwise free to move up and down for the passage of the air. A piece of wood is glued on the top of the leathers, to ensure that they shall drop flat and close the valve when the air is within.

A wire stop, s (Fig. 190), is driven into the board, to prevent the wood valves turning completely over, in which case they would not again close when re-

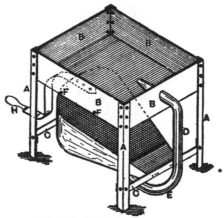

Fig. 192.—Small Portable Forge.

quired. The middle board has a block of wood fastened to it, for the reception of the screwed end of the pipe conveying the blast from the bellows to the hearth.

The three boards are fastened together by a piece of leather 14 in. wide, which goes all round them, and is securely nailed to their edges by 1-in. clout nails, placed in two rows, and as near together as possible. The leather of the bellows covering should be of good quality, and may be obtained at any leather-seller's. It is scarcely likely that a piece will be obtained sufficiently large to make it entire, so it may have to be joined. A strip of leather, 1 in. in width, is placed round the edge of each board over the leather covering, and the clout nails are driven through this and the leather covering into the boards. Before fixing the leather on to the boards, two rings of ¼-in. round iron bar, 14½ in. diameter outside, are inserted in each chamber. These are to keep the leather stretched outward, and to ensure it forming even creases when opening and closing. The two ends of the circular band of leather covering the bellows should be joined with copper rivets and washers, such as are used in leather hose, put as near together as possible.

The pipe leading the air blast from the bellows to the hearth is of ¾-in. iron tube, and is shown in section, with its fittings, by Fig. 191. At the bottom it is screwed into the wood block T, and at the top into the tuyere, J, through the iron band encircling the hearth, with a back nut and washer to keep it secure. The tuyere should be of thick wrought iron, and tapped to receive the end of the ¾-in. tube as shown. The forge is now complete, and it only remains to regulate the flow of air by putting weights on the top board of bellows. Weights should also be suspended from the bottom board sufficient to draw the lever up when pressed down.

Of course, the dimensions of the forge may be varied, and the material can even be made lighter; but, owing to the knocking about such a forge has to sustain, it will be best to keep as near as possible to the dimensions given.

Another portable forge (Fig. 192) is made of wrought iron, with the exception of the tuyere; this may be the hub of a plough or other wheel. The legs (A, Fig. 192) are of 1-in. angle iron 1 ft. 6 in.

long. The sides and end-plates are of 4⅛-in. by ⅛-in.
fender plate, and are respectively 18 in. and 15 in.
long. One of the end-plates is drilled through with
a 1¼-in. hole for the reception of the blast-pipe ᴅ
(Fig. 192). ᴄ, ᴄ are the stays as set out in Fig. 193;

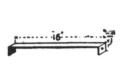

Fig. 193.—Stay of Portable
Forge.

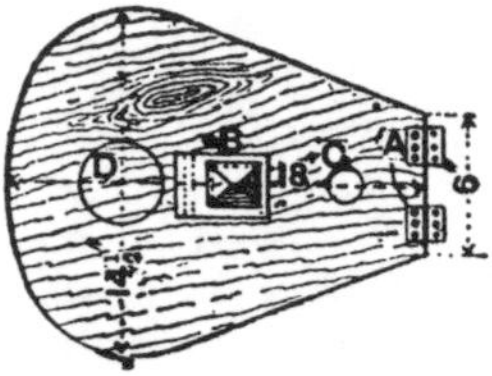

Fig. 194.—Plan of Portable
Forge Bellows.

they strengthen the legs and support the bellows.
The single-blast bellows, as shown in detail by Fig.
194, are made of two 1-in. pine boards, cut to the
dimensions given, and hinged by cast butts at ᴀ; ʙ
is the valve which is required in one board only; ᴄ is
the hole for the delivery-pipe; the bend with union
shown at ᴇ (Fig. 192) and ᴅ (Fig. 194) indicates the

Fig. 195.—Joint of Corner of Hearth.

position of the bellows spiral spring. The bellows,
which is made of basil leather, opens to 7½ in. ʜ
(Fig. 192) may be either a handle or a step, or a
combination of both. ꜰ, ꜰ (Fig. 192) show the rivets
which hold a ledge inside to support the bottom of
the forge. This bottom is of soft steel, 18 in. by 15 in.
The delivery-pipe is threaded at ɢ (Fig. 192) for 4
in., and a nut (not shown) on each side of the fender

plate holds it securely in its place. The bellows is secured by ordinary screws, which pass through the stays, but small bolts might be used with advantage. The whole thing is fixed together with round-headed rivets ½ in. by 3-16 in.; the sides may be filed to a mitre joint, see Fig. 195.

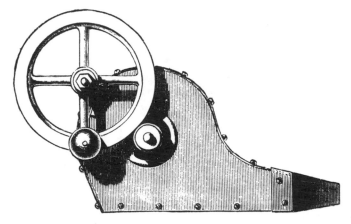

Fig. 196.—Side View of Continuous-blast Blow-bellows.

The construction of a continuous blast blow-bellows (see Figs. 196 and 197) will now be dealt with. These emit a continuous current of air instead of the intermittent current of the old-fashioned ones; instead of getting the draught from a 3-16-in. hole, or thereabouts, it is got through a hole 2½ in. wide and ¾ in. deep, and these bellows cost only about half as much.

To commence the construction of the bellows, cut out the sides and the bottom, but do not screw them together. Make a spindle (as Fig. 198 and 199), drill two holes in each side, one at each end, as shown, and tap them and screw a piece of wire to fit; cut it

into pieces about 5-16 in. long, and screw a piece into
each hole. Four pieces of tin, a little narrower than

Fig. 197.—Front View of Continuous-
blast Blow-bellows.

Fig. 198.—Spindle of
Blow-bellows.

the bellows, have corresponding holes punched in
them for the pieces of wire to slip through; put one

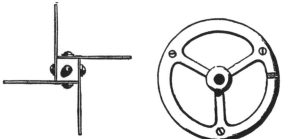

Fig. 199.—Side View of Blow-
bellows Spindle.

Fig. 200.—Brass Bearing
for Sides of Blow-bellows.

of them on, slip a washer over the wire, and then
rivet it over. Treat all in the same way, and then

screw the brass bearings (Fig. 200) to the sides, fit in
the iron spindle, and screw sides and bottom together,
afterwards screwing the piece of metal over the top.

Fig. 201.—Brass Spindle for
Blow-bellows Wheel.

Fig. 202.—Plate for Fixing Wheel
of Spindle.

The wheel will have to be bought. Fig. 201 is a
sketch of spindle for it to run on. Turn this up,
screw it at each end, fix it with a nut to the plate

Fig. 203.—Wood to Screw on
Spindle of Blower.

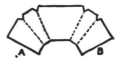

Fig. 204.—Pattern for
Nozzle of Blower.

(Fig. 202), put on the wheel, and keep it there by a
washer and another nut, then fit the knob on rather
loosely. But before fixing the wheel, turn a bit of
wood (Fig. 203) and over it put an indiarubber band,
and screw this on to the projecting end of the iron
spindle; fix the wheel against this tightly. In Fig.
204 is shown the shape of the nose-piece. When cor-
rectly cut out, bend this over at right angles at all
the dotted lines, and it will fit on the end of the bellows. Either rivet or solder together the two edges,
A and B, then drill it and screw it on. When this is
all done, turn the handle rapidly; the fan inside will

then revolve at a good rate, and a strong draught will be obtained. Of course, the fan can have five or even six wings, but in such a case it is advisable to strengthen the wings by soldering pieces of wire between them, as in Fig. 205.

Fig. 205.—Side View of Blow-bellows Spindle and Fan.

Another improvement is to turn a small groove in the iron wheel, and fix it a little further away from the iron spindle; turn up a smaller wheel, put a groove in it also, and screw it on to the end of the iron spindle; it could then be run with a band. It works very well, however, with the wheel fixed against an indiarubber-covered knob, as previously explained.

It is preferable to substitute gun-metal for the brass in all parts except the covering and nose-piece.

CHAPTER X.

MANIPULATING STEEL AT THE FORGE.

From the foregoing chapters it will have been seen that pure metallic iron has but little commercial use, and, in fact, in this state is comparatively unknown; it is when combined with carbon, sometimes modified by other elements, that pure iron becomes the iron of commerce, and is known as malleable iron, steel, and cast iron, as the proportion of carbon is increased. The great value of steel for toolmaking consists in a characteristic, possessed by no other substance, of becoming intensely hard when quickly cooled after it has been heated to a certain temperature. The pure, the mild steels, that nearly approach the condition of iron are ductile and weldable. On the other hand, their capacity for hardening and tempering diminishes with the comparative absence of carbon, which is the principal hardening element, though in no case does the proportion equal that in cast iron. In steel, carbon seldom amounts to more than 1.5 per cent. It is less than .1 per cent in the mildest plates.

In addition to carbon, but in a lesser degree, manganese, phosphorous and silicon are hardening constituents of steel. Within certain limits, the more these constituents are present, the lower the temperature of the cooling liquid employed, and the greater its power of absorbing heat, the more intense will be the hardness induced in the steel. Mushet steel, used for making turning tools, is produced by the addition of woolfram or tungsten, in the form of a metallic alloy, to steel. The resulting alloy is so hard that it does not require to be hardened by the tool maker.

There is, as regards chemical composition, very little difference between wrought iron and some of the mild steels. But when working there is a very essential difference between them. Wrought iron is never perfectly homogeneous, whilst mild steel is of the same character throughout. This difference is due to the altered condition in the processes of manufacture. The fluidity of cast iron is mainly due to the presence of its carbon, and in a lesser degree to its sulphur. These are removed from the iron in the processes of puddling; and one important result is the non-fusibility of the wrought iron at the temperature at which it is found best to work it. Wrought iron is never in a state of absolute fusion at any time during the process of its puddling. It is simply brought into a pasty condition, like a lump of dough. In order to render this material more homogeneous, the pasty mass is compressed under steam hammers or tilt hammers, and is passed beneath squeezers of different types, is cut up again and re-heated, and the operations of hammering, squeezing, and rolling are repeated, the homogeneous quality of the iron improving with each repetition of these operations. These sets of operations will be repeated three or four times in the case of good merchantable iron, and it is the cost of fuel and labor involved which renders wrought iron so much more costly than cast iron.

After the last piling, re-heating, and hammering processes have been gone through, the iron is run between grooved rollers of diminishing sizes, to impart the final sectional forms to the bars or plates required for the use of the smith. But even in the best wrought iron, owing to the absence of fusion, some of the oxide or scale, and some of the impurities originally present in the iron, or taken up in the process of puddling, become mechanically mixed with, and remain in the bars, which always remain laminated, causing the iron to become spilly, and to develop incipient fracture when wrought into structures. The best wrought iron can never be depended on entirely for absolute homogeneity. But for the average work of the smith it holds its own, because of its ductility, weldability, and the general ease with which it can be fashioned into intricate forms.

The Bessemer and Siemens steels are free from this lamination, because during the process of fusion all scale or oxide is expelled; this is one reason why the mild steels have superseded wrought iron largely for boiler-makers' work, and for cranks and similar structures, where lamination would be fatal to strength and durability.

Steel being homogeneous—that is, having no lamination—is eminently adapted for forging light and delicate work, where strength, rigidity, and lightness are required in combination. While wrought iron can be worked almost at the fusing point, each different sample of steel seems to work best at a particular temperature, differing from that of other samples, but never beyond a full red heat. Steel takes a much higher polish than wrought iron, and is therefore better suited to work where good finish is necessary.

Whether steel is more troublesome to work than iron depends on the nature of the forging and on the quality of metal. For small model work, steel is by far the easier, because there is no grain to open out, besides the superior rigidity, and so forth. In large and heavy forgings there is no advantage to be gained on this score. Steel forgings of moderate size and thin sections have to be worked at a lower temperature than iron, so a larger number of heats must be taken in the former than in the latter. For the same reason the various operations should be performed more rapidly while the steel retains its heat.

There is more initial difficulty in welding steel

than iron, due to the differences in various samples of steel. Once the best welding heat for any bar of steel is known, there is no more trouble experienced in welding pieces from that bar. Sand alone is used as a flux for welding iron; for steel a mixture of sand and common salt is better.

There is a greater difference of opinion as to the working of steel than there is in regard to the working of iron. The practice of allowing steel to soak in the fire, approved by some, is denounced by others. The temperature to which steel can be raised without burning it is also a matter of dispute. The practice of hardening and tempering steel opens up an unlimited field of discussion. The reasons are that steels vary in quality much more than wrought iron, and since the peculiar value of steel is due to its chemical and molecular composition, slight differences in which cause great changes in the material, and as even slight and sudden alterations in temperature are sufficient to entirely change their arrangement, it is easy to understand why, though not how, the practical working of the material is affected. Partly because of these differences and consequent differences in treatment demanded, some makes of steel are considered superior to others. Thus, a man accustomed to work in one quality mainly, and having adopted certain modes of treatment with the best results, may find the same modes do not give equally good results with another quality; he may then condemn the steel, when in reality the fault lies in wrong treatment. Every bar of new steel should be worked tentatively in order to discover the best heat and the best way to work that particular brand. Unless this is done, failure to obtain the best results will frequently follow. The practice of upsetting steel is deprecated by some. But if the steel is of good quality it will upset just as well as iron.

Steel should be made as hot as the metal will safely

bear, but it must not be overheated, or it will become burnt. A higher temperature can be used on steel required for large forgings than for steel used for light work generally, and for cutting tools. Burnt steel under the hammer will crumble to pieces as though it were cast iron, and will show a coarse granulated fracture. There are, however, degrees in burning; the steel may be burnt only slightly on the surface, so slightly that it does not fracture, or, if fractured, does not show this coarsely crystalline structure; yet its quality for cutting instruments will be sensibly impaired. The temperature at which overheating occurs varies, of course, with different qualities. If scales form and fall off, the steel is, as a rule, overheated. It is then almost impossible to restore its quality. If not burnt very badly, a good hammering on the anvil will improve it considerably.

Steel, even more than iron, should be turned around in the fire to keep the heat uniform. The blast should be slackened after the edges have become red-hot. A full cherry-red is usually considered the proper heat for forging—but this expression is rather vague, and the temperature will vary with different qualities. Hammering should not be continued after the steel has lost its redness.

There is a temperature in steel corresponding with what is termed in iron a "black heat"—at which it is not safe to work it. Experiments show that a steel plate heated, and allowed to cool, suffers no diminution of strength, but that while cooling, and while at a blue heat, any hammering or bending seriously injures the metal. The blue heat corresponds with any temperature between about 470° and 600°.

Steel used for making tools is classified according to the percentage of carbon it contains, to which the following list is a guide. *Razor temper steel* (1½ per cent carbon) is so easily spoilt by being overheated that it can be worked only in the hands of a very skilful workman. When properly heated, it will do twice the work of ordinary tool steel for turning chilled rolls, etc. *Saw-file temper steel* (1⅜ per cent carbon) requires careful treatment, and although it will stand more heat than razor steel, should not be heated above a cherry red. *Tool temper* steel (1¼ per cent carbon) is the most useful for turning tools, drills, and planing-machine tools, and it may be forged by ordinary workmen. It is possible, with great care and skill, to weld cast steel of this temper. *Spindle temper* steel (1⅛ per cent carbon) is very useful for circular cutters, large turning tools, taps, screwing dies, etc. This temper requires considerable care in welding. *Chisel temper* steel (1 per cent carbon) combines great toughness in the unhardened state, with the capacity of hardening at a low heat. It is consequently well adapted for tools when the unhardened part is required to stand the blow of a hammer without splitting, but where a hard cutting edge is required, such as cold chisels, hot setts, etc. *Sett temper* steel (⅞ per cent carbon) is adapted for tools, such as cold setts, the unhardened parts of which have to stand very heavy blows. *Die temper* steel (¾ per cent carbon) is the most suitable for tools of which the surface only is required to be hard, and where the capacity to withstand great pressure is of importance, such as stamping or pressing dies, boiler cups, etc. The last two tempers may be easily welded by a mechanic accustomed to work cast steel.

The process of hardening, as commonly understood by smiths, means the heating of a piece of steel to redness and quickly plunging it into a cooling liquid, usually either water or oil. Hardening steel often causes it to crack and warp. On immersing the steel into the cooling medium, the outer covering is rapidly cooled off first, and shrinks upon the interior.

The shrinkage puts the outside in tension. Presently the interior cools, but it is prevented from free shrinkage by its union with the exterior, and is thus itself put in tension. Then one of two things may happen: either there will be a condition of permanent tension, productive of warping or curvature, or the stresses will find relief in fracture.

Steel that is heated to redness and allowed to cool slowly is said to be annealed. Steel may be annealed by making it red hot and allowing it to cool between hot cinders. Or it may be left in a low fire until the fire has gone out and the cinders have become cold. Or it may be enclosed in a box with charcoal powder, raised to a red heat, and allowed to become cold. By hardening, steel is made intensely hard, by tempering it is made softer and less brittle, but yet it remains very hard; by annealing, it is brought into its softest possible condition.

The principal hardening agent is cold water; salt water, lukewarm water, and oil are sometimes used. Mercury is also very efficient, but its expense precludes its use for ordinary work, and for most purposes pure cold water only is used. For light and delicate work oil is generally considered preferable, and it is customary to use oil or tallow in preference to water for all delicate work. In order to lessen the liability to curvature, long narrow articles are immersed perpendicularly instead of horizontally or diagonally in the fluid, so that its effect may be evenly distributed over the whole of the surface. Steel is apt to crack if it is taken out of the water before being thoroughly quenched, or if the water level is kept at one place; it should therefore be moved slightly up and down in the water. When dipping an article of unequal thickness on the edges, the thicker edge, as a rule, should be dipped first, to lessen risk of cracking. Smiths have an opinion that water which has been long used is preferable to fresh water, so they do not change the water in their hardening tanks, but simply add sufficient fresh to make up for waste. This preference may be due to the fact that warming of the water by immersing red-hot metal drives off the air contained in it, and allows the fluid to come into more intimate contact with the surface of the steel. The belief that boiling the water for hardening steel is an improvement may be explained in the same way.

It is not necessary that hardening should always be done in a liquid. A thin heated plate placed between two pieces of cold metal will become hardened as effectually as if immersed in water or oil. This is often done, because it tends to lessen risk of warping in a plate.

Hardening by means of hammer blows is of occasional service to increase the elasticity and hardness of a plate or lamina of steel. Its effect is similar to that of cold rolling and wire drawing, and is removed by annealing. If hammer hardening is prolonged too far the metal is fractured; annealing must therefore be resorted to before this stage is reached. The range of temper obtainable in hammer hardening is not great, and it has a limited value, being confined chiefly to laminated springs.

Tempering means that the hardened steel is slightly re-heated, and when at a certain known temperature, indicated by a shade of color which appears on its brightened surface, it is plunged into a cooling liquid, or in some few cases is allowed to cool gradually in air. This heat for tempering differs in almost every variety of tool or piece of mechanism. The tints through which steel passes from the lower to the higher temperature are straw, gold or yellow, chocolate, purple, violet, and blue. The greatest hardness and elasticity combined is obtained by tempering at a straw color. Hardening by quenching at a red heat makes a tool intensely hard, but brittle.

Tempering by quenching at a blue makes it elastic, but soft. Between these extremes lies the whole practice of hardening and tempering.

All cutting tools of the same type are not tempered alike. Thus, a tool for working hard cast steel will be tempered harder than one for working gray cast iron. A tool tempered a straw color is harder than one tempered a blue; so that if tools for hard steel are tempered to a straw, those for soft iron and brass are tempered at a tint approaching purple.

As an example of hardening and tempering, a cold chisel is the tool selected. The scale is removed from the surface, and its cutting end, to the length of about a couple of inches, is then first heated to a cherry red in a clear fire, afterwards quenching in water, and thus hardened. It is taken out and rapidly brightened with a bit of grindstone or emery, in order that the rapidly changing hues may be observed the better. The cooling of the end only lasts for an instant, as the heat of the shank at once raises the temperature of the end for tempering, until the instant arrives at which it must be quenched. The smith then plunges the entire chisel into the water, moving it to and fro until quite cold. The color for tempering in the case of a cold chisel is a deep straw inclining to purple, but, of course, the color will vary with different grades of steel.

Another way of tempering small tools is to heat to redness in the forge fire a bar of iron, and lay the tools upon it until they reach the color required, and to then quench them. If the bar is made red hot at one end only, the tools can be gradually slid along toward that end and so slowly heated thoroughly through, until they reach the precise tint desired for tempering.

A bath of molten lead is a good heating agent for articles that are of unequal thickness; these can thus be heated uniformly. The lead is prevented from oxidation by covering its surface with powdered charcoal. The temperature of a bath of molten metal is, of course, uniform, and by making alloys of lead and tin in various proportions, an extensive range of temperature is obtainable. The table below serves to show what range can be got by such tempering baths.

Drills for cutting iron are tempered to a dark straw at the cutting edges. The remarks made in reference to the hardening and tempering of a cold chisel apply equally to drills for iron. Drills for hard steel are heated and quenched in a lump of lead, and not tempered afterwards.

Axes are hardened and tempered very much like chisels. They are heated first to redness, and quenched in water to a depth of two or three inches. A face is polished, and the changing tints observed until the appearance of a deep blue, when total immersion is made for temper. As for other tools, different shades of blue, inclining towards a brown straw, will be required for different grades of steel.

TEMPERING STEEL.

Color.	Articles to be Tempered.	Composition of the Bath Lead.	Tin.	Tempera- ture in de- grees Fah.
Yellowish tint.	Lancets	7	4	420°
	Other surgical instruments	7½	4	430°
	Razors, etc............	8	4	442°
Pale yellow...	Penknives, and some implements of surgery	8½	4	450°
Straw yellow..	Larger penknives, scalpels, etc.............	10	4	470°

Color.	Articles to be Tempered.	Composition of the Bath. Lead.	Tin.	Temperature in degrees Fah.
	Scissors, shears, garden hoes, cold chisels, etc.	14	4	490°
Brown yellow.	Axes, firmer chisels, plane irons, pocket-knives, etc..........	19	4	509°
Light purple..	Table-knives, large shears, etc..........	30	4	530°
Dark purple..	Swords, watch-springs, etc.	48	4	550°
Clear blue....	Large springs, daggers, augers, fine saws, etc.	50	2	558°
Pale blue.....	Pit saws, hand saws, and some springs....	Boiling linseed		
Greenish blue.	Articles which require to be somewhat softer	oil. Molten lead.		600° 612°

Mill picks are hardened only, and not tempered. They are heated to a dark red, and quenched, the temper thus obtained not let down, as is the case with most of the tools already noticed. Pure soft water is quite suitable for these, though some smiths use mixtures of salt, alum, sal-ammoniac, etc.

Springs are hardened in the usual way by heating to a cherry red, and quenching in water. Then they are smeared with tallow or lard, and heated over the fire, moving them to and fro until the tallow catches fire, and blazes and burns off. The springs are then laid upon the forge, or in the ashes to cool down. If the work is of irregular thickness, the burning of the oil should be repeated two or three times. Small springs made in quantities are often put into a sheet-iron pan and covered with oil, and held over the fire until the oil blazes and burns off. Moving and shaking the pan about causes the temper to be more uniform. In the case of heavy springs the operation may be repeated two or three times.

Screw taps are conveniently heated in an iron tube, large enough to allow not only of the admission of the tap, but also of the tongs by which it is held. The tap is first heated gradually and very slowly, and equally throughout, to a dull red in the tube. If heated rapidly, the edges of the threads will be made hotter than the interior, and being too hard, will probably crumble off in use. It must be an invariable rule to harden and temper taps at the lowest heat practicable. A dull red must not be exceeded. It is better to make two or three attempts, increasing the heat each time, rather than to overheat the tap, which is plunged vertically into water and held there until quite cold. Afterwards the flutes are brightened and the tap heated in the tube to a light straw. Some use linseed oil baths for hardening taps and dies. The points of the threads will be protected if coated with soft soap, or with a paste made of prussiate of potash and flour, or yeast.

Screwing dies are heated to a cherry red, and hardened in salt water. To diminish the risk of cracking, they may be covered with prussiate of potash or with a paste of soap and oil. The faces are polished, and to temper them the dies placed on a piece of hot iron, taking care to turn them over and over until they are of a straw color. A bath of lin- seed oil may be used for cooling. Worn dies are, as a rule, re-cut, but before this can be done, the temper must be completely drawn by annealing the dies by heating them to a light cherry red in a clear fire and allowing them to cool slowly. Other tools, such as broaches, milling cutters, reamers, and lip drills, when worn, are similarly annealed preparatory to recutting. Afterwards they are hardened and tempered just as in the case of new tools.

Case hardening is a method commonly used for rendering the surface of wrought iron as hard as tempered steel. Case hardening means that just the outer skin of iron is hardened, and made of the nature of steel. Only wrought iron can be treated thus. A mere film of surface hardening may be effected by heating the iron red-hot, rolling it in powdered yellow prussiate of potash, and quenching in water. When the hardening is required to extend to a greater depth, the work is enclosed in an iron receptacle along with leather clippings, bones, horn, and yellow prussiate of potash, and heated for from twenty to forty hours. The work is then cooled in water. The advantages of case hardening are that the toughness of the wrought iron is combined with a durable wearing surface as hard as steel; and that the first cost of the forgings, and of the cost of their being tooled and finished into shape, is less than the cost of steel forgings. Case hardening is adopted in link-reversing gear for engines, for the eyes and working faces of levers, for pins or pivots, and so forth. To case harden at the forge, have ready a quantity of yellow prussiate of potash powdered very fine in an iron tray. Heat the work in the clear fire to red heat and with a spoon strew thickly over the surface of the forging, and, if practicable, roll the forging also in the potash. The work is re-heated and time given to allow the powder to fuse and run freely over the surface, then the forging is quenched, and this hardens it.

INDEX.

154